# SRA Imagine It!

# Skills Practice

## Annotated Teacher's Edition

**Level 5**
**Book 1**

## McGraw Hill SRA

Columbus, OH

**SRAonline.com**

 **SRA**

Send all inquiries to this address:
SRA/McGraw-Hill
4400 Easton Commons
Columbus, OH 43219-6188

ISBN: 978-0-07-610496-3
MHID: 0-07-610496-6

1 2 3 4 5 6 7 8 9 QPD 13 12 11 10 09 08 07

## Unit 1 Heritage

# Unit 2 — Energy at Work

# Unit 3 Making a New Nation

Name _____ Date _____

# Root Words

**Focus**

Many words contain **root words** that come from languages other than English. For example, *bicycle* and *recycle* both contain the Greek root *cycl,* which means "circle." Knowing the meaning of a root can help you learn the meanings of words that use the same root. However, a word's literal meaning is often different from a word's common English meaning. *Cyclone* literally means "to go around in a circle." Its actual meaning is "a storm of winds that revolve around a center, such as a tornado."

**Practice**

**Each word is followed by its root word and the root's definition. Choose two words from the box that use the same root word, and write them on the lines.**

| thermal | enact | produce | thermostat |
|---------|-------|---------|------------|
| dislocate | locate | react | conduct |

**1.** education; root word *duc,* meaning "to lead"

produce        conduct

**2.** action; root word *act,* meaning "to do"

react        enact

**3.** location; root word *loc,* meaning "place"

locate        dislocate

**4.** thermometer; root word *therm,* meaning "heat"

thermostat        thermal

**Apply** Each word below is followed by a literal definition. Use a dictionary to find its actual definition, and then use the word in a sentence.

**5.** allocate = to place

**Possible Answer** The manager allocated funds for a yearly company picnic.

**6.** activate = to drive or do

**Possible Answer** He tried to activate the device but was unsuccessful.

**7.** egocentric = oneself being the center

**Possible Answer** Jeremy is very egocentric and thus not a very good teammate.

**8.** aqueduct = to lead water

**Possible Answer** The tour guide told us the aqueduct was important to the process of supplying the city with its water.

Name _____ Date _____

# Selection Vocabulary

**propped** (propd) *adj.* supported by something under or against (page 24)

**edible** (ed' • ə • bəl) *adj.* fit or safe to eat (page 27)

**lingered** (lin' • gərd) *v.* past tense of **linger**: to be slow in leaving (page 28)

**inspired** (in • spīrd') *v.* influenced (page 29)

**unjustly** (un • just' • lē) *adv.* unfairly (page 30)

**persecuted** (pûr' • si • kyo͞ot' • əd) *v.* past tense of **persecute**: to treat in a cruel and unjust way (page 30)

**logic** (lo' • jik) *n.* a way of thinking about something (page 31)

**apparently** (ə • par' • ənt • lē) *adv.* as far as one can judge by the way things appear (page 33)

**assumed** (ə • so͞omd') *v.* past tense of **assume**: to take for granted (page 34)

**reality** (rē • al' • i • tē) *n.* something actual or real (page 34)

**Practice** Write the vocabulary word next to the group of words that have a similar meaning.

**1.** without cause; unfairly; unequally _____unjustly_____

**2.** thought; judgement; reason _____logic_____

**3.** encouraged; motivated; uplifted _____inspired_____

**4.** seemingly; evidently _____apparently_____

**5.** actuality; fact; existence _____reality_____

**6.** delayed; lagged _____lingered_____

**7.** tormented; mistreated; wronged _____persecuted_____

8. eatable; consumable _____edible_____

9. supposed; presumed _____assumed_____

10. supported; up against _____propped_____

**Apply** Fill in each blank with a word from the word box that best completes each sentence.

| lingered | unjustly | reality | assumed | apparently |
|----------|----------|---------|---------|------------|
| logic | propped | edible | persecuted | inspired |

11. Mr. Sheer _____assumed_____ we had studied for the test.

12. This is _____apparently_____ the tallest hill in the city.

13. I _____propped_____ up my sprained ankle on the chair.

14. The meat was left out all night and is no longer _____edible_____.

15. We will have to use _____logic_____ to solve this puzzle!

16. The crowd _____unjustly_____ taunted the visiting team.

17. The _____reality_____ is that we cannot afford a new car.

18. Kristy had the thought that her brother was _____persecuted_____ by the bullies at school.

19. The speech _____inspired_____ the entire class to stand up and clap.

20. Because she did not want to leave, she _____lingered_____ by the door.

Name _____  Date _____

# Author's Point of View

**Focus**  Writers must decide from whose point of view they will tell a story.

- **First-person point of view** is told through the eyes of a character in the story. First-person narrators use words such as *I, me, we, us, our,* and *my.*

- **Third-person point of view** is told through the eyes of a narrator who is outside the story. Third-person narrators use words such as *he, she, her, them, theirs, his,* and *hers.*

**Practice**  **Read the following paragraph from "The Land I Lost: Adventures of a Boy in Vietnam." Decide whether the author used a first-person point of view or a third-person point of view. Then, rewrite the paragraph using the opposite point of view.**

1. "My father, like most of the villagers, was a farmer and a hunter, depending upon the season. But he also had a college education, so in the evenings he helped to teach other children in our hamlet, for it was too small to afford a professional schoolteacher."

Point of view: First-person

New Paragraph: **Possible Answer** His father, like most of the villagers, was a farmer and a hunter, depending upon the season. But he also had a college education, so in the evenings he helped to teach other children in his hamlet, for it was too small to afford a professional schoolteacher.

**Apply**

Read each paragraph, and determine whether it is in the first-person or third-person point of view. Then, rewrite the paragraph, using the opposite point of view.

**2.** When Shelly moved to a new neighborhood, she was not sure she liked the kids who lived there, but when she got an invitation to her next-door neighbor's birthday party, she made several new friends.

Point of view: third-person

New Paragraph: When I moved to a new neighborhood, I was not sure I would like the kids who lived there, but when I got an invitation to my next-door neighbor's birthday party, I made several new friends.

**3.** "Never in my wildest dreams did I expect to see you here!" shouted Andy in surprise. I just stood up and smiled. It was good to see Andy after so many months.

Point of view: first-person

New Paragraph: "Never in my wildest dreams did I expect to see you here!" shouted Andy in surprise. His friend stood up and smiled. He was glad to see Andy again after so many months.

Name _____ Date _____

# Recording Concept Information

**As I read the selection, this is what I added to my understanding of heritage.**

- "The Land I Lost: Adventures of a Boy in Vietnam" by Huynh Quang Nhuong

**Possible Answer** I learned of the importance of preserving one's heritage and remembering family members.

- "Our Song" by Angela Johnson

**Possible Answer** People can learn a great deal about heritage from their families, even if their lives are very different.

- "The Dancing Bird of Paradise" by Renee S. Sanford

**Possible Answer** People can keep their cultural traditions alive even through difficult times.

- "From Miss Ida's Porch" by Sandra Belton

**Possible Answer** Storytelling is a good way for people to learn about their heritage.

- "In Two Worlds: A Yup'ik Eskimo Family and History of the Tunrit" by Aylette Jenness and Alice Rivers

**Possible Answer** It is important to remember and preserve one's heritage as the world around us changes.

# Knowledge about Heritage

• This is what I know about heritage before reading the unit.

**Possible Answer** Heritage is about your family and ancestors.

It is about traditions like songs and recipes passed down from

generation to generation.

_____

_____

_____

• These are some things about heritage that I would like to talk about and understand better.

**Possible Answer** What is my heritage and how far back does

my family go? How can you learn about heritage if you do not

know it?

_____

_____

_____

_____

Reminder: I should read this page again when I get to the end of the unit to see how much my ideas about heritage have changed.

**Name** _____ **Date** _____

# Ideas about Heritage

Of the ideas discussed in class about heritage, these are the ones I found most interesting.

**Possible Answer** Our family is much more than just our relations. Almost everything about our culture and heritage filters through our family in the form of stories and habits.

_____

_____

_____

_____

_____

_____

_____

_____

_____

_____

_____

_____

## Ideas about Heritage (continued)

**Write down the ideas you found most interesting about the selection "The Land I Lost: Adventures of a Boy in Vietnam." Discuss your ideas with the class.**

**Possible Answer** Our heritage makes us individuals while at the same time unifies all of us. We have a heritage that is our own, but we also have a shared heritage with people in our town, our state, our nation, even with everyone in the world.

**Name** _____ **Date** _____

# Writing a List

**Think**

**Audience: Who** will read your list?

**Possible Answer** I will read it.

**Purpose: What** is your reason for making a list? **Possible Answer**
The list will help me brainstorm ideas for a story.

**Prewriting**  **Using the lines below, brainstorm five topic ideas
for a story about an accomplishment of one of your
family members. Then, choose one idea and write
a pro and a con about using it for your topic.**

**Possible Answers**

Idea #1 My uncle moved to Mexico and became an artist.

_____

Idea #2 My mom went back to school so she could become a
nurse.

Idea #3 My little sister's soccer team just won a tournament.

_____

Idea #4 My great-grandparents traveled on a ship from Spain to
reach America.

Idea #5 My mom gives blood once a month at the clinic where
she works.

Pro: My uncle paints great pictures of Mexico.

_____

Con: I do not know my uncle very well.

_____

## Revising
**Use this checklist to revise your list.**

- [ ] Do the ideas in your list follow the writing assignment?
- [ ] Have you made a second list of pros and cons for each topic idea?
- [ ] Have you worked with others, sharing your list to get feedback about your ideas?
- [ ] Have you decided which suggestions you will follow and which ones you will disregard?

## Editing/Proofreading
**Use this checklist to correct mistakes.**

- [ ] Are any words misused or repeated?
- [ ] Have you checked for mistakes in spelling or capitalization?
- [ ] Have you capitalized proper nouns, literary titles, nationalities, ethnicities, languages, and geographic names and places?

## Publishing
**Use this checklist to prepare your list for publication.**

- [ ] Brainstorm possible publication methods with your group.
- [ ] Share your list with the class.

Name _____ Date _____

Name _____ Date _____

# Spelling

**Focus**

- **Compound words** consist of two smaller words that have been combined to form one larger word. These two words keep the same spelling in the compound word.
- **Root words** were formed from words of other languages, such as Greek and Latin. Understanding and identifying root words and their meanings can help you spell many new words. Here are some roots in the spelling words and their meanings:

*sol* = alone    *scop* = to see    *stella* = star

**Word List**

1. skateboard
2. rattlesnake
3. mountainside
4. solo
5. telescope
6. peppermint
7. solitary
8. outstanding
9. constellation
10. stellar
11. desolate
12. solitude
13. underground
14. periscope
15. earthquake
16. breakfast
17. scope
18. sweatshirt
19. microscope
20. thunderstorm

**Practice** The following compound words are missing one of their base words. Write the missing word on the line.

1. _____ rattle snake
2. out _____ standing
3. _____ skate board
4. _____ break fast
5. thunder _____ storm
6. _____ pepper mint
7. _____ under ground
8. mountain _____ side
9. _____ earth quake
10. sweat _____ shirt

**Fill in the appropriate root word and write the resulting spelling word on the line.**

11. _____sol_itary   solitary

12. tele_____scop___e   telescope

13. con_____stella___tion   constellation

14. de_____sol___ate   desolate

15. micro_____scop___e   microscope

16. _____sol_itude   solitude

17. peri_____scop___e   periscope

18. _____sol_o   solo

19. _____stella_r   stellar

20. _____scop_e   scope

**Apply** On the line, write the spelling word that contains one of the base words in the following compound words

21. rainstorm   thunderstorm

22. underwater   underground

23. surfboard   skateboard

24. sideways   mountainside

25. outdoors   outstanding

26. earthworm   earthquake

27. spearmint   peppermint

28. shirtsleeves   sweatshirt

Name _____ Date _____

# Common Nouns and Proper Nouns

**Focus**

**Nouns** name people, places, or things.

- A **common noun** is used to name a general, or nonspecific, person, place, or thing.
- teacher, library

- A **proper noun** is used to name a particular, or specific, person, place, or thing.
- Ms. Alvarez, Cook County Library

**Practice** Circle the nouns in the following sentences.

1. For nearly eighty (years,) (Pluto) was known as the ninth (planet) in our (solar) (system.)

2. (Clyde Tombaugh) discovered the tiny frozen (sphere) in 1930.

3. Recently, though, (scientists) have decided that (Pluto) is too small to be labeled a (planet.)

4. (Planets) like (Earth,) (Mars,) or (Jupiter) are much larger than (Pluto.)

5. (Pluto) is now officially known as a *dwarf* (planet.)

**Apply** Each pair of words below should include a common noun followed by a related proper noun. For example, *book* might be followed by *My Side of the Mountain.* Fill in the missing half of each pair below.

## Possible Answers

| Common Noun | Proper Noun |
|---|---|
| 6. country | France |
| 7. former president | Abraham Lincoln |
| 8. river | Colorado River |
| 9. mountain | Mt. Rainier |
| 10. student | Shelby |
| 11. day | Saturday |
| 12. relative | Uncle Ricardo |
| 13. city | New York |
| 14. school | Southeast High School |
| 15. holiday | Memorial Day |

Name _____ Date _____

# Prefixes *tele-* and *dis-*

**Focus**

- The prefix **tele-** means "far." Adding *tele-* to a base or root word changes its meaning. For example, *vision* is the ability to see; *television* is the device used to receive images broadcast over long distances.

- The prefix **dis-** means "not" or "the opposite of." Adding *dis-* to a base word often creates an antonym, or a word with the opposite meaning. For example, *disagree* is an antonym for *agree*; *disadvantage* means the opposite of *advantage*.

**Practice**    Add the prefix *tele-* or the prefix *dis-* to each base word below, and then write the new word's definition on the line. Use a dictionary if you need help.

**1.** content <u>discontent</u>

     **Possible Answer** not satisfied or pleased

**2.** conference <u>teleconference</u>

     **Possible Answer** a conference among people who are far from one another

**3.** comfort <u>discomfort</u>

     **Possible Answer** a feeling of uneasiness or something disturbing

**4.** communication <u>telecommunication</u>

     **Possible Answer** communication over long distances

**5.** continuous <u>discontinuous</u>

     **Possible Answer** something broken or interrupted

**Apply** Five base or root words and their meanings are given below. Add the prefix *dis-* or the prefix *tele-* to each base or root word, and then use the new word correctly in a sentence. Remember that a word's literal meaning is often different from its actual meaning.

6. connected = joined _disconnected_

   **Possible Answer** We disconnected the hose from the faucet.

7. phone = device for transmitting sound _telephone_

   **Possible Answer** The telephone is a great way for some people, who live far from one another, to communicate.

8. photo = picture of a person or thing _telephoto_

   **Possible Answer** T. J. used a telephoto lens to get close-up pictures of distant objects.

9. scope = extent or range of view _telescope_

   **Possible Answer** With his telescope, Nitesh could see the rings of Saturn.

10. approved = agreed to _disapproved_

    **Possible Answer** The teacher disapproved of the student's actions.

Name _____ Date _____

# Selection Vocabulary

**Focus**

**Senegal** (Sen' • i • gôl) *n.* a country in Africa (page 44)

**lavender** (la' • vən • dər) *n.* a plant with fragrant purple flowers (page 47)

**delicate** (de' • li • kət) *adj.* small or dainty (page 48)

**ship** (ship) *v.* to send by ship, train, truck, or airplane (page 50)

**traders** (trā' • dərz) *n.* plural of **trader:** a person who buys and sells things as a business (page 51)

**surrounded** (sə • round' • əd) *v.* past tense of **surround:** to be on all sides (page 51)

**mist** (mist) *n.* a cloud of tiny drops of water or other liquid in the air; fog (page 53)

**ignores** (ig • norz') *v.* pays no attention to (page 53)

**quivers** (kwi' • vərz) *v.* shakes slightly (page 54)

**Practice** Write the vocabulary word that best matches the underlined word or phrase in each sentence below.

1. The six of us <u>were on all sides</u> of the kitten as it played with a piece of string. _____surrounded_____

2. A field of <u>fragrant purple flowers</u> filled the countryside with a pleasant scent. _____lavender_____

3. At the toy convention, hundreds of <u>people who buy and sell</u> had set up booths. _____traders_____

4. My dog's entire body <u>shakes slightly</u> when he knows he is about to get a treat. _____quivers_____

*Skills Practice 1* • Vocabulary

**5.** The patrons were cooled by <u>drops of water in the air</u> drifting

from a nearby fountain. _____mist_____

**6.** We need to <u>send</u> these supplies by airplane, or they will

not arrive in time. _____ship_____

**7.** When the train passes by her apartment, Natalie <u>pays no</u>

<u>attention to</u> the noise. _____ignores_____

**8.** After he bumped the table in the museum, Paul broke the

<u>small and dainty</u> vase. _____delicate_____

**9.** His family is from <u>a country in Africa</u>. _____Senegal_____

**Apply** Draw a line to match each word on the left to its definition on the right.

10. mist

11. ship

12. ignores

13. lavender

14. surrounded

15. quivers

16. delicate

**a.** shakes slightly

**b.** small or dainty

**c.** a plant with fragrant purple flowers

**d.** to send by ship, train, truck, or airplane

**e.** was on all sides

**f.** a cloud of tiny drops of water in the air; fog

**g.** pays no attention to

Name _____ Date _____

# Formulating Questions and Problems

**A good question or problem to investigate:**

**Possible Answer** What is it about my heritage that makes me different from my classmates? What is it that makes us similar?

_____

_____

**Why this is an interesting question or problem:**

**Possible Answer** It provides a direct connection to the unit. It is also an opportunity to get to know more about our class and about ourselves.

_____

_____

**Some other things I wonder about this question or problem:**

**Possible Answer** Will this help us learn more about our community? Will we be able to make connections between our own personal heritage and our communal heritage?

_____

## Formulating Questions and Problems (continued)

**My investigation group's question or problem:**

**Possible Answer** What is each group member's family history? Where do the branches of their family tree go? How does this make each member unique? Or do they have a common heritage with others in the group?

**What our investigation will contribute to the rest of the class:**

**Possible Answer** This will enable us to get to know each other better as individuals and as a collective group. We will learn more about what makes each of us who we are.

**Some other things I wonder about this question or problem:**

**Possible Answer** How does our class compare to our community? Are we the continuance of a long cultural tradition, or does our heritage signal change?

Name _____ Date _____

# Writing a Summary: One Text

**Think**

**Audience: Who** will read your summary?

**Possible Answer** I will.

**Purpose: What** is your reason for writing a summary?

**Possible Answer** I will use my summary to help my small group summarize "Our Song."

**Prewriting**  Summarizing can help you study by making the text easier to understand. Summaries can also tell others about what you have read. Choose one page from "Our Song," and reread it. On the lines provided, write three ideas or events from the page you chose.

**Possible Answers**

Page: _____50_____

Idea/Event #1: Josie's "dream cousins" have become real to her. _____

_____

Idea/Event #2: Josie is given a tour of the village by her cousins. _____

_____

Idea/Event #3: Josie does not want to wear a hat or shoes. _____

_____

**What is the page's main idea or event?**

Josie wants to be like her cousins because she thinks they have a lot of freedom.

**On a separate sheet of paper, write a short paragraph summarizing the page you read.**

## Revising

**Use this checklist to revise your summary.**

☐ Does your summary have a main idea?

☐ Is your main idea a single sentence that describes the story?

☐ Do your details support the main idea?

☐ Are your details told in an order that makes sense?

## Editing/Proofreading

**Use this checklist to correct mistakes.**

☐ Have you checked the spellings of proper names against the original text?

☐ Have you used correct punctuation for each sentence?

☐ Have you checked for spelling errors?

☐ Have you used correct sentence structure, including subject and predicate?

## Publishing

**Use this checklist to publish your summary.**

☐ Print or neatly rewrite your summary.

☐ Share your summary with the class.

Name _____ Date _____

# Spelling

**Focus**

• A prefix changes the meaning of the base word it precedes. Identifying prefixes and understanding their meanings can help you figure out the meaning and spelling of a difficult or unfamiliar word. The prefix **tele-** means "far," or "at a distance." The prefix **dis-** means "not or not having". It negates the meanings of the base word. These prefixes do not change the spellings of the base words.

• **Root words** were formed from words of other languages, such as Greek and Latin. Understanding and identifying root words and their meanings can help you spell many new words. Here are some roots in the spelling words and their meanings:
**graph** = write; **imag** = likeness; **nat** = born; **phon** = sound; **vis** = see; **photo** = light; **gram** = letter, written; **imag** = likeness; **nat** = born; **ord** or **ordin** = order; rank

**Word List**

1. disorder
2. telegraph
3. image
4. imagination
5. nationality
6. telephone
7. dishonest
8. television
9. disadvantage
10. disagree
11. telephoto
12. national
13. imagine
14. nation
15. telecast
16. discontinue
17. nationalize
18. telegram
19. imaginary
20. international

**Practice**

On the lines, write all of the spelling words that contain the same root or base word as each of the following words. Some words will have more than one answer.

1. native    national, nation, nationalize,

international, nationality
_____

2. unimaginative

image, imagination, imagine, imaginary

3. autograph

telegraph

4. visual

television

5. grammar

telegram

6. symphony

telephone

7. ordinary

disorder

8. recast

telecast

9. continuation

discontinue

10. agreement

disagree

11. photograph

telephoto

12. advantageous

disadvantage

13. honesty

dishonest

**Apply** Add the prefix *tele-* or *dis-* to each of the following base words to create one of the spelling words and write it on the line.

14. gram        telegram

15. cast        telecast

16. order       disorder

17. agree       disagree

18. honest      dishonest

19. continue    discontinue

20. graph       telegraph

21. advantage   disadvantage

22. phone       telephone

Spelling • *Skills Practice 1*

Name _____ Date _____

# Subjects, Predicates, and Simple Sentences

**Focus**

A **simple sentence** contains only one independent clause with a subject and a predicate.

- The **subject** is the part of the sentence that tells who or what.

- The **predicate** is the part of the sentence that describes or tells what the subject does.

- A **simple subject** is a the key noun or pronoun in a simple sentence that does something or is described.

- A **compound subject** is two or more simple subjects linked by a conjunction.

- The **predicate** in a simple sentence can also be simple or compound.

- **The students** visited a nature preserve.

- The students **visited a nature preserve.**

- **The students** visited a nature preserve.

- The **students** and their **teacher** visited a nature preserve.

- The students **visited a nature preserve** and **had a picnic.**

**Practice** The following sentences are simple sentences. Circle the subject and underline the predicate in each sentence.

1. Griots are traveling musicians and poets.

2. They play an important role in West African culture.

3. The history and traditions of West African people were shared by word of mouth for many centuries.

4. The griots' songs and poems helped keep the stories alive.

5. The stories helped preserve the culture's rich heritage.

**Apply**  Identify the subject and predicate in each sentence below. Then, label each subject **S** for simple or **C** for compound. Do the same for each predicate. Write an **S** next to each sentence that is a simple sentence.

6. _____ Subject: ___C___ Predicate: ___S___
Because they love the sport, Lauren and Jackie play softball every other Saturday.

7. ___S___ Subject: ___S___ Predicate: ___C___
Their team won six games and lost three last year.

8. ___S___ Subject: ___C___ Predicate: ___S___
Mrs. Suarez and her son, Will, have attended every game and several practices.

9. _____ Subject: ___S___ Predicate: ___S___
Because they are polite, they bring sandwiches for everyone after the game.

10. ___S___ Subject: ___S___ Predicate: ___C___
Jackie sprained her ankle and missed two games at the start of this season.

11. ___S___ Subject: ___C___ Predicate: ___C___
She and a team member collided and knocked each other to the ground.

12. ___S___ Subject: ___S___ Predicate: ___S___
Lauren played Jackie's position at first base for the next two games.

Name _____ Date _____

# Multiple-Meaning Words, the Prefix *un-*, and the Prefix *en-*

**Focus**

- **Multiple-meaning words** are words with more than one meaning, but the same word origin. You will often need to look at context clues to figure out which meaning is being used.

- The prefix **un-** means "not or the opposite of." For example, the word *unbalance* means "not balanced or in disorder."

- The prefix **en-** means "to put into," or "to cause to be." For example, *ensure* means "to cause to be sure."

**Practice** Each word below uses the prefix *en-* or *un-*. Use your knowledge of the base word's meaning to write an original sentence for each word. Identify the base words that are multiple-meaning words and provide two definitions for each word.

**1.** *entangle* _____ **Possible Answer** The fish became entangled in the tentacles of the jellyfish. _____

**2.** *encircle* _____ **Possible Answer** The river encircles the village. to surround; a sphere, ring-like object or formation _____

**3.** *unfair* _____ **Possible Answer** The decision was unfair. a gathering of buyers and sellers for trade, just and impartial _____

**4.** *uncomfortable* _____ **Possible Answer** The hard cushions of the couch made it uncomfortable. _____

**Apply** The following sentences contain multiple-meaning words. The words and their possible meanings follow the sentence. Circle the letter of the meaning that is used in the sentence. If the prefix *en-* or *un-* can be added to the word, then add the prefix and write the definition of the resulting word on the line.

In the <u>center</u> of the <u>case,</u> there was an emblem representing the owner.

**5.** center
   (a.) the middle part
   b. a building used for a particular function

_____

**6.** case
   a. an instance or occurrence
   (b.) small, portable container

**Possible Answer** to enclose

Though Tim had a good <u>excuse</u> for his absence, we were still <u>forced</u> to abruptly cancel the event.

**7.** excuse
   (a.) apology or to try to remove blame from
   b. to allow to leave

_____

**8.** forced
   (a.) to compel
   b. power or strength

**Possible Answer** enforce: to impose upon a person

Name _____     Date _____

# Selection Vocabulary

**Focus**

**kimono** (ki • mō' • nə) *n.* a loose robe that is tied with a sash (page 64)

**phonograph** (fō' • nə • graf') *n.* an instrument that reproduces sound from records (page 64)

**startled** (stär' • tld) *adj.* excited by sudden surprise or alarm (page 66)

**internment** (in • tûrn' • mənt) *adj.* confined or impounded, especially during a time of war (page 6•)

**barrack** (bar'• ək) *adj.* providing temporary housing; very plain and uniform (page 69)

**sweltered** (swel' • tərd) *v.* past tense of **swelter:** to suffer, sweat, or become faint from heat (page 69)

**ascend** (ə • send') *v.* to climb (page 71)

**donned** (dond) *v.* past tense of **don:** to put on (page 72)

**soloed** (sōl' • ōd) *v.* past tense of **solo:** to dance or perform alone (page 72)

**enrich** (en • rich') *v.* to make better by adding something (page 73)

**Practice**  Circle the word in parentheses that best completes each sentence.

**1.** My dad replaced his (barrack, (phonograph)) with a CD player years ago.

**2.** Heather (soloed, (donned)) a hat and gloves before heading out into the cold.

**3.** The hikers ((sweltered,) startled) under the punishing desert sun.

**4.** The crowd cheered as the guitarist (startled, (soloed)) during the last half of the song.

**5.** The festival begins when the hot-air balloons ((ascend,) enrich) into the sky.

**6.** A server wearing a (barrack, (kimono)) served us sushi.

7. The sailors were (startled, sweltered) by a sudden wave that crashed against the boat.

8. Julio used slides to (enrich, phonograph) his presentation.

9. The (kimono, barrack) provided shelter for many families escaping the flood.

10. The (internment, startled) camp was the home for many families during World War II.

**Apply** Write the word from the box that matches each definition below.

| barrack | phonograph | donned | ascend | enrich |
|---|---|---|---|---|
| soloed | kimono | internment | sweltered | startled |

11. _____internment_____ confined or impounded

12. _____enrich_____ to make better by adding something

13. _____phonograph_____ an instrument that reproduces sound from records

14. _____sweltered_____ suffered or became faint from heat

15. _____kimono_____ a loose robe that is tied with a sash

16. _____barrack_____ providing very plain temporary housing

17. _____donned_____ put on

18. _____soloed_____ danced or performed alone

19. _____startled_____ excited by sudden surprise

20. _____ascend_____ to climb

Name _____ Date _____

# Making Inferences

Writers often do not include every detail about a character or an event in the story. Readers must use clues from the text to make inferences in order to complete the picture. **Making inferences** means using the writer's clues and your own prior knowledge and experiences to develop a better understanding of the character or event.

**Read the following sentences from "The Dancing Bird of Paradise." Make an inference about Sahomi based on each sentence and write it on the line.**

**1.** "Twenty minutes was all [Sahomi] had alone with her teacher, but she stayed much longer each afternoon, watching and copying the other students, learning their dances as well as her own."

Inference: ___**Possible Answer** Sahomi was dedicated and hard-working.___

**2.** "When she taught her students, Sahomi explained the story and meaning behind each dance."

Inference: ___**Possible Answer** Sahomi believed that knowing a dance's history was as important as learning its steps.___

**Apply**   **Read the description of each character below. Then write a short paragraph inferring how the character feels without actually stating it.**

**3.** a dog who wants to play

**Possible Answer** Rex bounded into the room, searching for his favorite toy. He found it lying in the corner of the room. Rex grabbed the toy in his mouth and ran over to Sammy. He dropped the toy at Sammy's feet, and then looked up with his tail wagging.

**4.** a performer who is nervous

**Possible Answer** Sarah stood at the edge of the stage waiting to go on next. She wrung her hands and looked out at the huge audience. She had never performed before so many people. She closed her eyes and tried to calm down.

**5.** a boy excited to see his favorite movie

**Possible Answer** When Johnny heard his favorite movie was showing at the local theatre, he could hardly believe it. He saved his allowance for the entire week to buy his movie ticket. The movie was showing at noon, but Johnny arrived at ten. He wanted to make sure he had a good seat.

Name _____ Date _____

# Making Conjectures

**Our question or problem:**

**Possible Answer** What do immigrants bring with them when they come to a new country?

_____

_____

_____

_____

**Conjecture (my first theory or explanation):**

_____

**Possible Answer** Immigrants bring their customs like traditional dances, foods, celebrations, and dress with them.

_____

_____

_____

_____

_____

**As you collect information, your conjecture will change. Return to this page to record your new theories or explanations about your question or problem.**

# Establishing Investigation Needs

**My group's question or problem:**

**Possible Answer** What do immigrants bring with them when they come to a new country?

_____

_____

_____

**Knowledge Needs—Information I need to find or figure out in order to investigate the question or problem:**

**A:** **Possible Answer** I need to know why they immigrated.

**B:** **Possible Answer** I need to know where they came from.

**C:** **Possible Answer** I need to know why their customs are so

**D:** important to them.

**E:** _____

## Possible Answers

| Source | Useful? | How? |
|---|---|---|
| Encyclopedias | yes | to show where the immigrants came from |
| Books | yes | information on immigration |
| Magazines | | |
| Newspapers | | |
| Video and Audio Clips | yes | program on immigration |
| Television | | |
| Interviews or observations | | |
| Museums | yes | for graphics, art, and examples of dress |
| Other: | yes | for information on immigration |

Inquiry • *Skills Practice 1*

**Name** _____ **Date** _____

# Writing a Summary: Two Texts

**Think**

**Audience: Who** will read your summary?
**Possible Answer** a classmate

**Purpose: What** is your reason for writing a summary?
**Possible Answer** I want to tell my readers about two
stories I have read.

**Prewriting**

When summarizing more than one text, you need to
show similarities and differences. Comparing details
what the texts have in common. Contrasting details
how they are different. Use the organizer to compare and contrast
"Our Song" with "The Dancing Bird of Paradise."

| **Subject 1 Our Song** | **Similarities** | **Subject 2 The Dancing Bird of Paradise** |
|---|---|---|

**Possible Answers**

Josie learns a traditional song; Josie is a fictional character; Josie is ten years old throughout the story.

They both live with a grandparent; they both leave America and travel to their grandparent's home country; they both learn about their cultures.

Sahomi learns a traditional dance; Sahomi is a real person; the story follows Sahomi into adulthood.

**Write two to three paragraphs summarizing the similarities
and differences between the two stories.**

## Revising
**Use this checklist to revise your summary.**

☐ Does your summary have a main idea?

☐ Do the details support your main idea?

☐ Did you present your comparisons and contrasts in a logical order?

☐ Do your comparisons and contrasts make sense?

☐ Have you included adjectives and adverbs to make your writing more interesting?

## Editing/Proofreading
**Use this checklist to correct mistakes.**

☐ Are your adjectives and adverbs, including comparatives and superlatives, used correctly?

☐ Have you checked for errors in spelling, capitalization, and punctuation?

☐ Have you read your summary several times to check for mistakes?

## Publishing
**Use this checklist to share your summary.**

☐ Neatly type or rewrite your summary.

☐ Share your summary with someone who might like either of the stories.

**Name** _____ **Date** _____

# Spelling

**Focus**

A prefix changes the meaning of the base word it precedes. Identifying prefixes and understanding their meanings can help you figure out the meaning and spelling of a difficult or unfamiliar word. Many words feature the prefixes *un-* and *en-*. The prefix **un-** means "not," or "the opposite of." The prefix **en-** has several meanings: "to put in or into"; "to cause to be"; "thoroughly." These prefixes do not change the spelling of the base words.

**Word List**

1. enrich
2. unpleasant
3. endanger
4. enable
5. uninspired
6. unlikely
7. encompass
8. unmarked
9. enlarge
10. ungrateful
11. encode
12. enlighten
13. unlimited
14. unsatisfied
15. unsweetened
16. enjoy
17. encourage
18. uneaten
19. enrage
20. unnamed

**Practice**

Add the prefix *un-* or *en-* to the following base words and write the resulting spelling words on the lines.

1. _____named    unnamed
2. _____eaten    uneaten
3. _____joy    enjoy
4. _____satisfied    unsatisfied
5. _____lighten    enlighten
6. _____grateful    ungrateful
7. _____rich    enrich
8. _____danger    endanger
9. _____inspired    uninspired
10. _____compass    encompass

11. _____large          enlarge

12. _____code          encode

13. _____limited          unlimited

14. _____sweetened          unsweetened

15. _____courage          encourage

16. _____rage          enrage

17. _____likely          unlikely

18. _____marked          unmarked

19. _____able          enable

20. _____pleasant          unpleasant

**Apply** The following words are misspelled. Write the correctly spelled spelling word on the line. If the word is already correct, write correct.

21. ennamed          unnamed

22. ungrateful          correct

23. enmarked          unmarked

24. unrage          enrage

25. enlarge          correct

26. unjoy          enjoy

27. uncompass          encompass

28. ensatisfied          unsatisfied

29. enlighten          correct

30. unrich          enrich

# Adjectives and Adverbs

**Focus** **Adjectives** modify nouns.

- Adjectives show what kind, how many, and which one.
- **colorful** shirts; **several** children
- Proper adjectives, like proper nouns, are always capitalized.
- **French** toast; **Jewish** deli

**Adverbs** modify verbs, adjectives, and other adverbs.

- Adverbs show how, when, where, and to what extent.
- walked **slowly;** bowled **yesterday;** jumping **around; very** quiet

**Practice** Circle the adjectives, and underline the adverbs in the following paragraph.

(Each) spring, Washington, D.C. is filled with the (colorful) blossoms of (Japanese) (cherry) trees. In 1912, (Tokyo's) mayor generously donated (three-thousand) trees. They clearly symbolized the (growing) friendship between Japan and America. A (two-week) festival is held annually to celebrate the (blossoming) trees and (Japanese) culture.

**Read each numbered sentence. On the first line, write** *adjective* **or** *adverb.* **On the second line, write the word or phrase from the box that describes how the adjective or adverb functions in the sentence.**

| how<br>when | what kind<br>how many | where<br>which one | to what extent |
|---|---|---|---|

1. Tom, Shane, and Wylie were **deeply** involved in a **card** game.

   **a.** *Deeply* is an _____adverb_____; it tells _____to what extent_____.

   **b.** *Card* is an _____adjective_____; it tells _____what kind_____.

2. They **always** relaxed in Shane's **tree** house when it was **too** hot to play basketball.

   **a.** *Always* is an _____adverb_____; it tells _____when_____.

   **b.** *Tree* is an _____adjective_____; it tells _____what kind_____.

   **c.** *Too* is an _____adverb_____; it tells _____to what extent_____.

3. **Suddenly,** a **loud** crash echoed through Shane's **normally** calm backyard.

   **a.** *Suddenly* is an _____adverb_____; it tells _____how_____.

   **b.** *Loud* is an _____adjective_____; it tells _____what kind_____.

   **c.** *Normally* is an _____adverb_____; it tells _____to what extent_____.

4. The **two** boys **carefully** climbed **down** from the tree house.

   **a.** *Two* is an _____adjective_____; it tells _____how many_____.

   **b.** *Carefully* is an _____adverb_____; it tells _____how_____.

   **c.** *Down* is an _____adverb_____; it tells _____where_____.

Name _____ Date _____

# Suffixes -*ant*, -*y*, and -*ity*

**Focus**  The suffix -**ant** means "being in a particular state" or "one who does something." For example, adding the suffix -*ant* to the word *serve* changes it to *servant,* or "one who serves."

The suffix -**y** means "having the quality of, state." For example, someone who has *luck* is *lucky.*

The suffix -**ity** means, "the quality or condition of." The suffix converts certain adjectives into nouns. For example, something that is *necessary* is a *necessity.*

**Practice**  Complete each sentence below with a word that uses the suffix -*ant*.

1. Someone who assists is an _____ assistant _____.

2. Someone who immigrates is an _____ immigrant _____.

3. Someone who occupies a room is an _____ occupant _____.

4. Someone who inhabits a place is an _____ inhabitant _____.

5. Someone who sells merchandise is a _____ merchant _____.

**Complete each sentence below with a word that uses the suffix -*y* or -*ity*.**

6. Something that has the quality of being fun is _____ funny _____.

7. Something that is real represents _____ reality _____.

8. Something that is considered abnormal is an _____ abnormality _____.

9. When the sun is shining outside it is _____ sunny _____.

10. Someone who is civil has _____ civility _____.

**Apply**   Read the following root words and their definitions. Use each root to create a word that ends with the suffix in parentheses, and then use the new word in a sentence. Use a dictionary if you need help.

**11.** vac = empty (-ant)

**Possible Answer** The house next door was vacant for nearly a year.

**12.** gust = sudden burst (-y)

**Possible Answer** The gusty winds caught us by surprise, and the umbrella blew away.

**13.** dorm = sleep (-ant)

**Possible Answer** The dormant volcano began rumbling to life.

**14.** bulk = large in size (-y)

**Possible Answer** The bulky load was almost too much for the ox to carry.

**15.** defy = challenge (-ant)

**Possible Answer** Audrey had a defiant look on her face as she defended her little brother.

**16.** able = having skill to accomplish a task (-ity)

**Possible Answer** He had the ability to be a great dancer.

**Name** _____  **Date** _____

# Selection Vocabulary

**Focus**

**attitude** (at' • ə • tōōd') *n.* a way of acting, thinking, or feeling (page 84)

**claim** (klām) *v.* to declare as one's own (page 85)

**magnificent** (mag • ni' • fə • sənt) *adj.* outstanding; excellent (page 85)

**spellbound** (spel' • bound) *adj.* fascinated; filled with delight or wonder (page 86)

**civilizations** (si' • və • lə • zā' • shənz) *n.* plural of **civilization**: an advanced human society in which agriculture, trade, government, art, and science are highly developed (page 86)

**section** (sek' • shən) *n.* a part of an area (page 87)

**concert** (kon' • sûrt') *n.* a musical performance (page 87)

**finest** (fī' • nəst) *adv.* best; most excellent (page 88)

**forbidden** (fər • bi' • dən) *adj.* off-limits (page 88)

**trolley** (trol' • ē) *n.* a streetcar that runs on tracks and gets its power from an electric wire overhead (page 90)

**Practice**  **Write the word from the Focus box that best fits each clue.**

1. It is one part of a building, a city, or any other area.

   What is it? _____ section _____

2. The Egyptians and the Mayans had famous ones.

   What are they? _____ civilizations _____

3. It is the best ice cream you have ever eaten.

   Which word compares it to other ice creams? _____ finest _____

**4.** A positive one is always better than a negative one.

What is it? _____attitude_____

**5.** This musical event can take place in an auditorium or a stadium.

What is it? _____concert_____

**6.** During the most dramatic part of a movie, your mouth hangs open, and you do not want to blink.

What are you? _____spellbound_____

**7.** Clang! Clang! Clang! Next stop, Telegraph Hill!

Where might you hear this? _____trolley_____

**8.** Do not enter! Stop! You are not allowed inside!

What kind of place would have these messages? _____forbidden_____

**9.** A lost glove waits quietly in a Lost and Found box.

What does it need someone to do to it? _____claim_____

**10.** Critics love it! Audiences agree. It is an excellent film.

What word describes this movie? _____magnificent_____

**Apply**  **Select the word that completes each sentence.**

**11.** The auditorium was filled with _____magnificent_____ decorations.

**12.** The front _____section_____ of our yard has been dug up.

**13.** Keiko was _____spellbound_____ as she watched the magician.

**14.** To succeed in life, it is helpful to have a good _____attitude_____.

**15.** Mr. Pérez's bakery makes the _____finest_____ bread in town.

**16.** You cannot _____claim_____ that book because the library owns it.

Name _____ Date _____

# Describing an Object

**Think**

**Audience: Who** will read your description?

**Possible Answer** another student

**Purpose: What** do you want your description to do?

**Possible Answer** I want the reader to be able to clearly picture the objects I have described.

**Prewriting** Close your eyes and visualize the object you want to describe. This method will help you focus on the most important details. Use the following graphic organizer to plan your description.

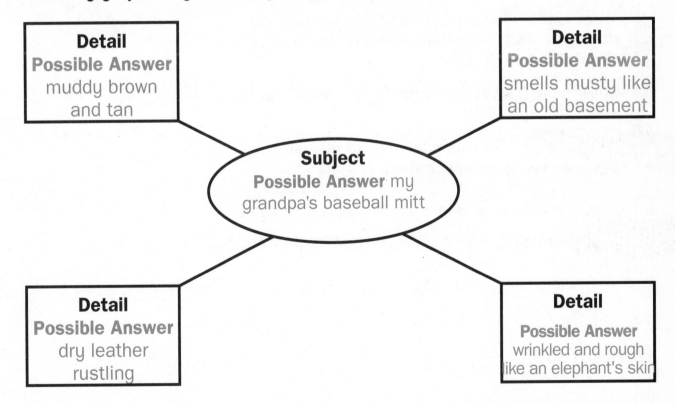

**Detail**
**Possible Answer** muddy brown and tan

**Detail**
**Possible Answer** smells musty like an old basement

**Subject**
**Possible Answer** my grandpa's baseball mitt

**Detail**
**Possible Answer** dry leather rustling

**Detail**
**Possible Answer** wrinkled and rough like an elephant's skin

## Revising
**Use this checklist to revise your description.**

- ☐ Are your details grouped in a way that makes sense?

- ☐ Have you chosen vivid and descriptive words so your reader can identify your object?

- ☐ Have you used sensory language or figurative language, such as similes and metaphors?

## Editing/Proofreading
**Use this checklist to edit your description.**

- ☐ Did you use commas and other punctuation correctly?

- ☐ Have you checked your description for capitalization or spelling errors?

- ☐ Have you read through your description several times to check for mistakes?

- ☐ Start making a list of the errors you are commonly making.

## Publishing
**Use this checklist to publish your description.**

- ☐ Neatly rewrite your final copy in cursive handwriting.

- ☐ Post your description and illustration in the classroom.

Name _____   Date _____

# Spelling

**Focus**
- Understanding and identifying suffixes and their meanings can help you determine the meaning and spelling of a difficult or unfamiliar word. Many words feature the suffixes -y, -ity, and -ant.
- The suffix **-y** means "having the quality of, state or condition."
- The suffix **-ity** means "state or quality of."
- The suffix **-ant** means "one who" when added to a verb to make a noun. It means "being in a particular state" or "one that does a particular action or promotes a particular state" when added to a word to make it an adjective.

**Word List**
1. modesty
2. vigilant
3. servant
4. necessity
5. civility
6. honesty
7. nobility
8. assistant
9. immigrant
10. lucky
11. messy
12. agility
13. rainy
14. pleasant
15. hostility
16. defiant
17. tasty
18. resistant
19. purity
20. formality

**Practice** Write the spelling word that results when the suffix -ity, -ant, or -y is added to the following base words or word parts.

1. formal        formality
2. necess        necessity
3. agile         agility
4. noble         nobility
5. hostile       hostility
6. civil         civility
7. pure          purity
8. resist        resistant

9. vigil    <u>vigilant</u>

10. please    <u>pleasant</u>

11. assist    <u>assistant</u>

12. serve    <u>servant</u>

13. immigrate    <u>immigrant</u>

14. defy    <u>defiant</u>

15. taste    <u>tasty</u>

16. rain    <u>rainy</u>

17. modest    <u>modesty</u>

18. luck    <u>lucky</u>

19. honest    <u>honesty</u>

20. mess    <u>messy</u>

 **Apply**   **Correct the misspelled words and write them on the line. If the word is already correct, write correct.**

21. servent    <u>servant</u>

22. honestty    <u>honesty</u>

23. nobilty    <u>nobility</u>

24. assistant    <u>correct</u>

25. pureity    <u>purity</u>

26. formalty    <u>formality</u>

27. modestity    <u>modesty</u>

28. messy    <u>correct</u>

Name _____ Date _____

# Commas

**Focus**

**Commas** are used to organize the thoughts and items in a sentence. They show the reader where to pause so that a sentence's meaning can be clearly understood.

- Use a comma to separate three or more items.

- I eat bananas**,** apples**,** and oranges.

- Use a comma after long introductory phrases or dependent clauses.

- **After we finished cleaning the house,** my dad and I relaxed.

- Use a comma and a conjunction to join two independent clauses.

- Luiz wants to play chess**, but** Shonda wants to play checkers.

- Use a comma when an interjection is not followed by an exclamation point.

- **Gosh,** I did not know that. **Hi,** Mr. Harris.

- Use a comma before and after an appositive.

- My friend, **Lacy,** is going to Kentucky.

**Practice**

**The commas are missing or used incorrectly in the following sentences. On a separate sheet of paper, rewrite each sentence so that it is correct.**

**1.** During our trip, to Texas we will drive through Tennessee, and Arkansas.
During our trip to Texas, we will drive through Tennessee and Arkansas.

**2.** Hildy put on, a coat a hat a scarf and mittens and, then she went outside.
Hildy put on a coat, a hat, a scarf, and mittens, and then she went outside.

**3.** Well that is a great a story but, I am not sure I believe it.
Well, that is a great story, but I am not sure I believe it.

**4.** After ten years, in college John my cousin is, about to graduate.
After five years in college, John, my cousin, is about to graduate.

**5.** We washed dried and peeled, the potatoes, before cutting them into small pieces.   We washed, dried, and peeled the potatoes before cutting them into small pieces.

**Apply** | Insert commas where they are needed in the following paragraph.

W. E. B. DuBois, an important American civil rights leader, was also a writer, poet, editor, and historian. DuBois graduated from Harvard University in 1890, and then he studied in Europe for a few years. After returning to the United States, DuBois became the first black man to earn a Ph.D. from Harvard. DuBois's most famous book, *The Souls of Black Folk,* was published in 1903. He was also a founding member of the NAACP, or the National Association for the Advancement of Colored People. When DuBois died in 1963, he was a citizen of Ghana, a country in Africa.

Name _____ Date _____

# Suffixes *-ence*, *-ing*, and *-ly*

- The suffix *-ence* means "state or quality of being." For example, *innocence* means "the quality of being innocent."

- When *-ing* is added to a verb, it forms the present participle. It can be used as a verb, adjective, or noun.

   I saw my friend **running** down the street. (participle)

   **Running** is good exercise. (noun)

   I bought a pair of **running** shoes. (adjective)

- The suffix *–ly* means "like or resembling." When added to a root or base word the suffix forms adjectives, as in *lovely,* or adverbs, as in *beautifully.*

**Practice**
Each sentence below contains a boldfaced word with one of the suffixes covered in this lesson. On the line, write *P* if the word is an adverb, *N* if it is a noun, or *A* if it is an adjective.

1. ___A___ Maurice uses a **shopping** cart when he goes to the store.

2. ___P___ I **slowly** licked the ice cream melting down the side of the cone.

3. ___A___ Sometimes Mr. Harrera uses a **sliding** scale to grade papers.

4. ___N___ The Fourth of July is a celebration of America's **independence.**

5. ___A___ You could still see the **dissolving** salt in the liquid.

6. ___N___ Before the trial, the defendant proclaimed his **innocence.**

**Apply**  Complete the "word-math" problems below. Then use each solution in a sentence.

**7.** evident + ence = <u>evidence</u>

<u>**Possible Answer** The detective found evidence that</u>

<u>helped solve the crime.</u>

**8.** unusual + ly = <u>unusually</u>

<u>**Possible Answer** I found an unusually large flower</u>

<u>growing in the woods.</u>

**9.** nurse + ing = <u>nursing</u>

<u>**Possible Answer** One career I have considered is nursing.</u>

**10.** selfish + ly = <u>selfishly</u>

<u>**Possible Answer** My brother acted selfishly when he</u>

<u>would not share his candy.</u>

**11.** comical + ly = <u>comically</u>

<u>**Possible Answer** Tom speaks comically whenever he</u>

<u>wants to get a laugh.</u>

**12.** sail + ing = <u>sailing</u>

<u>**Possible Answer** Sailing is my favorite pastime.</u>

Name _____ Date _____

# Selection Vocabulary

**Focus**

**vast** (vast) *adj.* great in size (page 101)

**tilted** (tilt' • ed) *v.* past tense of **tilt:** to raise one side of (page 101)

**withered** (with' • ərd) *v.* past tense of **wither:** to dry up from a loss of moisture (page 101)

**inhabit** (in • ha' • bət) *v.* to live in or on (page 103)

**role** (rōl) *n.* a position or function (page 109)

**luxury** (lug' • shoo • rē) *adj.* expensive (page 109)

**freighter** (frā' • tər) *n.* a ship used for carrying cargo (page 110)

**sewage** (soo' • ij) *n.* waste that is carried off in sewers and drains (page 111)

**lagoon** (lə • goon') *n.* a shallow body of water usually connected to a larger body of water (page 111)

**fluent** (floo' • ənt) *adj.* able to speak effortlessly (page 113)

**Practice** Write *T* in the blank if the sentence for the vocabulary word is correct. Write *F* if the sentence is false. For every *F* answer, write the word that fits the definition.

1. A freighter is a ship for carrying cargo. T _____

2. A luxury is something that gives pleasure but is not necessary.
   T _____

3. To inhabit means "to live in or on something."
   T _____

4. A lagoon is a function or a position. F role _____

**5.** Sewage is waste that is carried off in sewers or drains.

T _____

**6.** Fluent means "very great in size or number." F vast _____

**7.** Withered means "raised one side of." F tilted _____

**8.** A lagoon is a shallow body of water connected to a larger one.

T _____

**9.** One who is vast in a language can speak it effortlessly.

F fluent _____

**10.** Withered leaves are dried up from a loss of moisture.

T _____

**Apply** Circle the correct letter to answer each question below.

**11.** Which is an example of a *role*?
   **a.** the principal
   **b.** the filing cabinet

**12.** Which is an example of something that is *tilted*?
   **a.** a table with books on it
   **b.** a table on which balls always roll off one side

**13.** Which is an example of *inhabit*?
   **a.** the birds living in the tree
   **b.** the birds catching insects as they fly

**14.** Which is an example of something you would find in a *lagoon*?
   **a.** a rowboat
   **b.** a car

Name _____  Date _____

# Compare and Contrast

**Focus** Writers compare and contrast to paint a clearer picture of the people and things they are writing about.

- To **compare** means to tell how things, ideas, events, or characters are alike.

- To **contrast** means to tell how things, ideas, events, or characters are different.

**Practice** **Look through "In Two Worlds: A Yup'ik Eskimo Family," and contrast the Scammon Bay of Mary Ann's childhood and the Scammon Bay of today.**

1. In Mary Ann's time: **Possible Answer** There were few people living in Scammon Bay, and they moved when the seasons changed in order to catch animals for food to survive.

   Today: **Possible Answer** There are 350 people living in fifty-six houses in Scammon Bay, and they catch fish and sell them for money.

2. In Mary Ann's time: **Possible Answer** They lived in sod houses with mud floors and used seal oil in lamps for light. She was fifteen years old when she first saw an airplane.

   Today: **Possible Answer** A dish antenna provides television to all homes, satellite transmission provides telephone services, and small planes fly to Scammon Bay.

**Apply** Read each sentence, and determine whether it shows a comparison or a contrast. Then, rewrite each sentence reflecting the other term.

**3.** Dave and Ed both finished all their vegetables. comparison

**Possible Answer** Dave finished his vegetables, but Ed did not.

**4.** Martha plays the trombone, while Janet plays the cello. contrast

**Possible Answer** Both Martha and Janet play the cello.

**5.** I like to read mysteries just like my sister Gina. comparison

**Possible Answer** Unlike my sister Gina, I like to read mysteries.

**6.** Both cats and dogs make good pets. comparison

**Possible Answer** Cats make good pets, but dogs are hard to care for.

**7.** Jacob and Jason are twins, but Jacob is slightly taller. contrast

**Possible Answer** Jacob and Jason are identical twins.

**On a separate sheet of paper, write a paragraph comparing and contrasting yourself to a friend or relative. Be sure to include ways that you are similar and ways that you are different.**

Name _____ Date _____

# Describing an Event: A Magazine Article

**Think**

**Audience: Who** will read your magazine article?

Possible Answer my family

**Purpose: What** is your reason for writing a magazine article?

Possible Answer I want to tell readers about an important event from my family's history.

**Prewriting** **Magazine articles tell their readers about important events. The information in an article needs to be accurate and complete. Journalists use the following six questions to make sure their stories include all of the facts. Answer the questions to make sure your article will be accurate and complete.**

What happened? Possible Answer My great-great-great-grandparents moved to America.

Where did it happen? Possible Answer They arrived at Ellis Island before moving to Boston.

Who was involved? Possible Answer Patrick and Anna Moore, and their daughter Mildred

When did it happen? Possible Answer They arrived here in the 1890s.

Why did it happen? Possible Answer Patrick's brother had come to America earlier and encouraged them to follow him.

How did it happen? Possible Answer They traveled on a crowded ship across the Atlantic.

## Revising

**Use this checklist to revise your draft.**

☐ Have you varied the introductory phrases in your sentences so that your article does not sound repetitive?

☐ Have you varied sentence types to create rhythm and interest?

☐ Does your opening paragraph grab the reader's attention with an interesting lead?

☐ Have you used descriptive words?

## Editing/Proofreading

**Use this checklist to look for mistakes in your draft.**

☐ Have you spelled proper nouns consistently throughout the article?

☐ Have you checked the events in your story against the time line that you made?

☐ Have you checked your facts more than once?

## Publishing

**Use this checklist to share your draft.**

☐ Have a friend or classmate read your draft.

☐ Listen carefully to his or her suggestions, and decide which ones you will use.

Name _____ Date _____

# Spelling

**Focus** Understanding and identifying suffixes and their meanings can help you determine the meaning and spelling of a difficult or unfamiliar word. The suffix **-ly** changes an adjective into an adverb. It means "like or resembling." When the suffix **-ly** changes a noun to an adjective, it means "resembling." It rarely changes the spelling of the base word to which it is added. The suffix **-ence** means "state or quality of," and, when added to a word, makes the word a noun.

**Word List**
1. independence
2. finally
3. convenience
4. wisely
5. violence
6. timidly
7. absence
8. cautiously
9. turbulence
10. silently
11. emergence
12. desperately
13. excellence
14. accurately
15. difference
16. strictly
17. reference
18. beautifully
19. competence
20. directly

**Practice** Drop the suffix **-ly** from each word and write the resulting word on the line.

1. finally    final
2. wisely    wise
3. timidly    timid
4. cautiously    cautious
5. silently    silent
6. desperately    desperate
7. accurately    accurate
8. strictly    strict
9. beautifully    beautiful
10. directly    direct

**On the line, write the spelling word that results when the suffix *-ence* is added to the following base words or word parts.**

**11.** compete    competence

**12.** absent    absence

**13.** convenient    convenience

**14.** turbulent    turbulence

**15.** emerge    emergence

**16.** excel    excellence

**17.** refer    reference

**18.** independent    independence

**19.** violent    violence

**20.** differ    difference

 **Apply**   **Select the correct word from the parentheses that completes each sentence and write it on the line.**

**21.** The little boy smiled timidly (timid, timidly) at the doctor.

**22.** She sang the song beautifully. (beautiful, beautifully)

**23.** The dog cautiously (cautious, cautiously) sniffed the air before going outside.

**24.** The students read the book silently. (silently, silence)

**25.** The town sheriff strictly (strict, strictly) enforced the law.

**26.** They tried desperately (desperate, desperately) to save the man's life.

Name _____ Date _____

# Verbs, Verb Phrases, and Objects

- **Verbs** are words that show action or express a state of being.

- **Verb phrases** consist of one or more helping verbs used with an action or state-of-being verb.

- **Direct objects** are nouns and pronouns that receive the action of the verb.

- **Indirect objects** are nouns and pronouns for or to whom something is done.

- **Objects** are also the nouns and pronouns that appear in prepositional phrases.

- Malcolm **grew** tomatoes and peppers.
  Tomorrow **is** the last day of school.

- I **have picked** a book for my report.
  She **could see** the deer running.

- Pilar finished her **homework.**
  The artist sculpted a **statue.**

- Denzel told his **classmates** a joke.
  We made our **mother** dinner.

- Take me to the **mall.**
  The bird flew over my **head.**

**Practice**

In the following sentences, circle the verb or verb phrase, and underline the direct object(s) once and the indirect object(s) twice.

1. Natalie (waited) inside the cab.

2. Sometimes our garbage (smells) like rotten eggs.

3. Next year I (will read) Tom Sawyer.

4. The astronauts (could see) Earth from outer space.

**5.** The pitcher (threw) the batter a curve ball.

**6.** The concert (was held) near an old, abandoned factory.

**7.** Soon my order (will arrive) by special delivery.

**8.** Omar (drew) his friend a picture of some horses.

**Apply**   The verb or verb phrase in each sentence below has been boldfaced. On the first line, write *A* if it is an action verb or *S* if it is a state-of-being verb. One object in each sentence has also been boldfaced. On the second line, write *D* if it is a direct object, *I* if it is an indirect object, or *P* if it is the object of the preposition.

**9.** Verb: ____A____          Object: ____D____
The bus **carries students** to and from school every day.

**10.** Verb: ____S____          Object: ____P____
I **have been** sick with the **flu** for almost a week.

**11.** Verb: ____A____          Object: ____D____
Lina **sold** Enrique her old **watch.**

**12.** Verb: ____S____          Object: ____P____
The violinist **seemed** satisfied with her **performance.**

**13.** Verb: ____A____          Object: ____I____
Mr. Lin **has told Maxwell** a story about his childhood.

**14.** Verb: ____A____          Object: ____D____
John **understood** the **rules** before he began playing the game.

Name _____  Date _____

# Compound Words and the Prefix *in-*

- **Compound words** are words formed by combining two or more smaller words into one larger word. If you know the smaller words' meanings, you can often figure out the meaning of the compound. For example, a *backpack* is a pack you carry on your back.

- The prefix *in-* means "not," "lacking," or "lack of." Adding *in-* to a base word usually creates a word with the opposite meaning. For example, *incorrect* means "not correct," or the opposite of *correct*.

On the lines below, write definitions for each pair of words. Then write a definition for the compound word they form. Use a dictionary if you need help.

**1.** saw: _**Possible Answer** a device used for cutting wood_

dust: _**Possible Answer** fine dirt or residue made of tiny particles_

sawdust: _**Possible Answer** dust that is produced when wood is cut_

**2.** head: _**Possible Answer** part of the body that holds the brain_

ache: _**Possible Answer** soreness or pain_

headache: _**Possible Answer** having soreness or pain in the head_

**3.** hand: _**Possible Answer** part of the body with five fingers_

made: _**Possible Answer** created or designed_

handmade: _**Possible Answer** created by hand_

Add the prefix *in-* to the following words and use a dictionary to define each word.

4. difference    indifference

5. direct    indirect

6. dependent    independent

**Apply**    Add the prefix *in-* to each word below, and then use the new word in a sentence. Include the compound word listed in your sentence.

7. in complete — sandcastle

**Possible Answer** The sandcastle was still incomplete when a wave washed it away.

8. in direct — landmarks

**Possible Answer** We took an indirect route to Nashville so that we could see some historic landmarks.

9. in convenient — homework

**Possible Answer** It is inconvenient for me to come by your house after my homework is done.

10. in active — underground

**Possible Answer** The volcano had been inactive underground for many years before it finally erupted again.

Name _____ Date _____

# Selection Vocabulary

**Focus**

**dissolve** (di • zolv')
*v.* to mix into liquid
(page 138)

**retirement** (ri • tīr' • mənt) *n.* the
act of taking oneself away from
a job or occupation (page 139)

**inefficient** (in' • ə • fish' • ənt)
*adj.* not offering a good use of
money or effort (page 139)

**vents** (vents) *n.* plural of **vent:**
an opening through which a gas
passes (page 139)

**charged** (chärjd) *v.* past tense
of **charge:** to fill with electricity
(page 141)

**demonstration** (de' • mən •
strā' • shən) *n.* something that
explains, proves, or shows
something clearly (page 141)

**donors** (dō' • nərs) *n.* plural
of **donor:** a person who gives
something (page 142)

**electrocuted** (i • lek' • trə •
kyoot' • əd) *v.* past tense of
**electrocute:** to kill by means
of a very strong electric shock
(page 143)

**attracted** (ə • trak' • təd) *v.* past
tense of **attract:** to cause to
come near (page 144)

**insulators** (in' • sə • lā' • tərz)
*n.* plural of **insulator:** a material
that does not carry an electric
charge (page 144)

**Practice**  **Fill in each blank with the vocabulary word
that best completes the sentence.**

1. Mr. Flores gave a ___demonstration___ of how to perform CPR.

2. Delivering one pizza at a time would be an ___inefficient___
way to work.

3. With help from several ___donors___, the Debate Club
purchased a new podium.

**4.** My grandma's _____retirement_____ has given her more time for volunteering.

**5.** That new bird seed _____attracted_____ nearly a dozen yellow finches to our backyard.

**6.** _____Dissolve_____ the salt in the water before you add the yeast.

**7.** DeShawn _____charged_____ his cell phone's battery before leaving for work.

**8.** Dryer _____vents_____ carry warm, damp air outdoors.

**9.** The _____insulators_____ covering the wires were necessary to protect the workers working on the electric line from being _____electrocuted_____ .

**Apply**  **Write the vocabulary word that matches each definition below.**

**10.** _____vents_____ openings through which gases pass

**11.** _____demonstration_____ something that explains a process

**12.** _____insulators_____ materials that do not carry electrical charges

**13.** _____attracted_____ caused to come near

**14.** _____donors_____ people who give

**15.** _____dissolve_____ to mix into liquid

**16.** _____charged_____ filled with electricity

**17.** _____electrocuted_____ killed by a strong electric shock

**18.** _____inefficient_____ not offering a good use of money or effort

**Name** _____ **Date** _____

# Recording Concept Information

**As I read the selection, this is what I added to my understanding of energy at work.**

- "The Sparks Fly" by Ruth Ashby

  **Possible Answer** I learned that Benjamin Franklin invented many things, but his work with electricity is his most recognized accomplishment.

- "Tailing Tornadoes" by Trudi Strain Trueit

  **Possible Answer** I learned that the central U.S. is known as a Tornado Alley. Energy takes many forms and tornados and storms are one type.

- "Jake Drake Know-It-All" by Andrew Clements

  **Possible Answer** I learned that the scientific method is used to prove a hypothesis right or wrong. Electromagnets are another form of energy.

- "The Wind at Work" by Gretchen Woelfle

  **Possible Answer** I learned that people have always used wind energy to make their lives easier. Alternative energy sources will help to decrease the use of fossil fuels.

- "What are Food Chains and Webs?" by Bobbie Kalman

  **Possible Answer** I learned that food is another form of energy and that plants and animals are dependent upon one another to survive.

# Knowledge about Energy at Work

- This is what I know about energy at work before reading the unit.

  **Possible Answer** All living things have energy. Food is energy in the form of calories. Electric cars are an example of an alternative fuel source which is cleaner than burning fossil fuels.

- These are some things about energy at work that I would like to talk about and understand better.

  **Possible Answer** What are alternative forms of energy? Why do we not use more of them? How will the car change in the next 25 years? How will my daily energy use change in the next 25 years?

Reminder: I should read this page again when I get to the end of the unit to see how much my ideas about energy at work have changed.

**Name** _____ **Date** _____

# Ideas about Energy at Work

Of the ideas discussed in class about energy at work, these are the ones I found most interesting.

**Possible Answer** Benjamin Franklin was not only an active writer and politician, but he was a thoughtful scientist as well.

_____

_____

_____

_____

_____

_____

_____

_____

_____

_____

_____

_____

_____

_____

## Ideas about Energy at Work (continued)

**Write down the ideas you found most interesting about the selection "Tailing Tornadoes." Discuss your ideas with the class.**

**Possible Answer** Nature is easy to track through science, but it still can be unpredictable and dangerous. This lesson demonstrates that we should cooperate with nature, not attempt to conquer it.

Name _____ Date _____

# Scientific Process

**Think**

**Audience: Who** will read the report of your experiment?

**Possible Answer** another student

**Purpose: What** is your reason for conducting an experiment?

**Possible Answer** I want to find out whether my

hypothesis is correct or incorrect.

**Prewriting**

**It is important to follow the steps of the scientific process. Use the lines below to begin your experiment.**

Problem: **Possible Answer** Does water alone make iron rust?

Hypothesis: **Possible Answer** Water makes iron rust, but iron also needs air to rust.

Procedure: **Possible Answer** I used five glass jars of the same size and iron nails

about 2½ centimeters long and ½ centimeter in diameter, with the head about

1 centimeter in diameter. In Jar 1, I placed one nail in one ounce of water, uncovered.

In Jar 2, I placed four nails, touching, side by side, uncovered in one ounce of water. I

filled Jar 3 to the brim with water that I had boiled for ten minutes (to get the air out),

placed one nail inside, and sealed it tightly with its lid. I did the same for Jar 4, except

I used four nails, placed side by side, touching each other. In Jar 5, I placed a dry nail

that I had painted with nail polish into one ounce of water, uncovered.

**The final step in your experiment is to draw conclusions based on your observations. Do your observations support your hypothesis? Write a paragraph summarizing your conclusions.**

## Revising

**Use this checklist to revise the report of your experiment.**

☐ Have you referred to data and included your observations?

☐ Have you included all of your observations?

☐ Have you presented the steps of the scientific process in their proper order?

☐ Did you use transition words to show the sequence of events?

☐ Have you varied your sentence structure type and length so your report is interesting to read?

## Editing/Proofreading

**Use this checklist to correct mistakes.**

☐ Have you labeled the steps of the scientific process correctly?

☐ Did you check all capitalization, punctuation, and spelling?

☐ Have you read your report more than once to check for correctly applied rules for regular and irregular plurals?

## Publishing

**Use this checklist to publish your results.**

☐ Rewrite your report neatly, or type it on a computer.

☐ The final step in the scientific process is to share the results of your experiment with others. For example, you could read your report to the class.

Name _____ Date _____

# Spelling

**Focus**

• **Compound words** consist of two smaller words that have been combined to form one larger word. These two words keep the same spelling in the compound word.

• The prefix **in-** has several meanings. It means "not"; or it can mean "within," "into," or "on."

**Word List**

1. indefinite
2. doubleheader
3. eyewitness
4. inefficient
5. inaccurate
6. windshield
7. loudspeaker
8. undertake
9. headquarters
10. inexperienced
11. keyboard
12. infinite
13. inability
14. injustice
15. grasshopper
16. overindulge
17. insight
18. involuntary
19. newsbreak
20. inconsiderate

**Practice** Combine the two smaller words to make a compound word from the word list and write it on the line.

1. news + break = _newsbreak_

2. double + header = _doubleheader_

3. head + quarters = _headquarters_

4. key + board = _keyboard_

5. wind + shield = _windshield_

Add the prefix **in-** to the following base words to form words from the spelling list and write them on the lines.

6. finite _infinite_

7. accurate _inaccurate_

8. experienced _inexperienced_

9. efficient _inefficient_

10. justice _injustice_

**Apply** On the line, write the spelling word from the list that best fits each definition.

21. a breaking news story <u>newsbreak</u>

22. a board with keys on it <u>keyboard</u>

23. a witness who sees something firsthand <u>eyewitness</u>

24. an insect that hops over the grass <u>grasshopper</u>

25. to indulge too much <u>overindulge</u>

26. a double set of games played one after the other <u>doubleheader</u>

27. a speaker that makes your voice loud and easily heard <u>loudspeaker</u>

28. the place where the head part of a company has its quarters <u>headquarters</u>

29. part of a car that shields you from the wind <u>windshield</u>

30. to take on something, such as a new project <u>undertake</u>

**Use the following phrases and select the spelling word that fits the description best. Write the word on the line.**

31. not experienced <u>inexperienced</u>

32. not efficient <u>inefficient</u>

33. not voluntary <u>involuntary</u>

34. without ability <u>inability</u>

35. the opposite of justice <u>injustice</u>

36. not considerate <u>inconsiderate</u>

37. seeing into <u>insight</u>

38. not definite <u>indefinite</u>

39. not accurate <u>inaccurate</u>

40. not ending <u>infinite</u>

**Name** _____  **Date** _____

# Action Verbs

- **Action verbs** add energy and precision to sentences. The action of the verbs can express mental or physical action.

- Action verbs can be the main verbs in verb phrases.

- Action verbs can also be found in dependent clauses.

- I **understand** what you are saying.

- Ted has been **thinking** it over.

- I was relieved when Jen **asked** for help. It was cold because someone **opened** a door.

**Circle the action verbs in the paragraph below.**

Last week, our class (visited) the Science Museum. We (saw) several demonstrations that (used) electricity. My friend Lana was a volunteer in one of them. Her long hair (stood) up on end when a wand was (waved) over her head. Later, she (told) me that she (knew) what would (happen) because she had been to the museum before. I (hope) that next time I can (volunteer) for that experiment!

**Apply**  Write a sentence that contains an action verb for each noun listed below. Then, underline the action verbs in your sentences.

**1.** trees

**Possible Answer** The trees swayed in a strong breeze.

**2.** baseball

**Possible Answer** I threw the baseball to the catcher.

**3.** bus driver

**Possible Answer** Our bus driver smiles and says hello as each student boards.

**4.** light bulb

**Possible Answer** The light bulb burnt out soon after we installed it.

**5.** magazine

**Possible Answer** My magazine subscription expired last month.

**6.** freeway

**Possible Answer** Freeway traffic slowed to a halt because of an accident.

Name _____  Date _____

# Word Origins

**Focus** Recognizing and understanding **word origins** can help you understand new and unfamiliar words. For example, take the word *microscopic.* It contains the Greek root *scop.* This root means "to look at." The prefix *micro-* means "very small." Thus *microscopic* means "too small to be seen."

**Practice** The following words originate from the same language. They each contain a Latin root that has been defined for you. On the line, write a different word that uses the same root.

**1.** liberate

Latin root *liber* means, "to free":

**Possible Answers**
liberty, liberally

**2.** portable

Latin root *port* means "carry":

**Possible Answers**
import, transportation

**3.** reform

Latin root *form* means "shape":

**Possible Answers**
transform, uniform

**4.** prediction

Latin root *dic* means, "speak":

**Possible Answers**
dictate, dictionary

**5.** abrupt

Latin root *rupt* means, "to break":

**Possible Answers**
erupt, interrupt

**Apply** The words below are Greek in origin. The meanings of their roots, prefixes, and suffixes have been provided for you. Define each word based on the meanings of its parts. Check your answers in a dictionary.

**6.** the prefix *pro-* = in front of

Greek root *logue* = word

*prologue* = **Possible Answer** words at the beginning of a text

**7.** the prefix *dia-* = across or through

Greek root *meter* = measure

*diameter* = **Possible Answer** measurement across a circle

**8.** Greek root *path* = disease or illness

the suffix *-ology* = study or science of

*pathology* = **Possible Answer** the study of diseases

**9.** the prefix *syn-* = together

Greek root *chron* = time

the suffix *-ize* = to make

*synchronize* = **Possible Answer** to make things happen at the same time

**10.** Greek root *aero* = air

the suffix *-ate* = to make

*aerate* = **Possible Answer** cause something to have air in it

# Selection Vocabulary

**Focus**

**layer** (lā' • ər) *n.* one thickness of something (page 154)

**raging** (rā' • jing) *adj.* very active and unpredictable (page 155)

**survey** (sûr' • vā) *n.* an inspection or investigation (page 155)

**opposing** (ə • pōz' • ing) *adj.* opposite; completely different (page 156)

**prediction** (pri • dik' • shən) *n.* the act of telling something before it happens (page 156)

**severe** (sə • vir') *adj.* very serious; dangerous (page 157)

**stovepipe** (stōv' • pīp') *n.* a thin pipe connected to a stove that directs smoke or fumes out of an area (page 160)

**spiraling** (spī' • rəl • ing) *v.* moving in the shape of a spiral (page 160)

**inspiration** (in' • spə • rā' • shən) *n.* the stirring of the mind, feelings, or imagination, especially so that some good idea comes (page 160)

**alert** (ə • lûrt') *adj.* awake and prepared to act (page 161)

**Practice** Write the vocabulary word next to the group of words that have a similar meaning.

1. encouragement; stirring; prompting ___inspiration___

2. differing; conflicting; contradictory ___opposing___

3. serious; critical; risky ___severe___

4. aware; watchful; attentive ___alert___

5. wild; unpredictable; turbulent ___raging___

6. forecast; projection; speculation ___prediction___

7. piece; slab; level; ___layer___

8. winding; twisting; turning _____ spiraling _____

9. investigation; study; research _____ survey _____

10. chimney; smokestack _____ stovepipe _____

**Apply**   Draw a line to match each word on the left to its definition on the right.

11. prediction

12. survey

13. inspiration

14. layer

15. severe

16. stovepipe

17. alert

18. raging

19. spiraling

20. opposing

a. awake and prepared to act

b. one thickness of something

c. the act of telling something before it happens

d. very active and unpredictable

e. the stirring of the feelings or imagination

f. opposite; completely different

g. an inspection or investigation

h. moving in the shape of a spiral

i. a thin pipe connected to a stove that directs smoke out of an area

j. very serious; dangerous

Name _____ Date _____

# Formulating Questions and Problems

A good question or problem to investigate:
**Possible Answer** How does my behavior affect Earth?

_____

_____

_____

Why this is an interesting question or problem:
**Possible Answer** It is a direct connection between me and a topic of concern. It gives me the opportunity to see how I affect Earth.

_____

Some other things I wonder about this question or problem:
**Possible Answer** Does my behavior have a direct impact on the environment of my community? Does the behavior of my community have a direct impact on the environment of Earth?

## Formulating Questions and Problems (continued)

My investigation group's question or problem:

**Possible Answer** In what way can we change our behavior to improve our effect on the environment? Will these be passive changes, such as changing basic behaviors, or more active changes, such as forming a litter clean-up group?

What our investigation will contribute to the rest of the class:

**Possible Answer** We can provide ideas for others on how to improve their behavior. We can help others consider ideas that they might not have discovered.

Some other things I wonder about this question or problem:

**Possible Answer** Can we change the general attitude of our community? Are there ways we can bring about change in others by changing our behavior?

Name _____ Date _____

# Gardener's Almanac

**Think**

**Audience: Who** will read your article?

**Possible Answer** my teacher and other students

**Purpose: What** is your reason for writing a gardening article?
**Possible Answer** I want to share my knowledge

about growing lima beans.

**Prewriting** When you use someone else's knowledge or ideas, you must give that person credit. Find some information about lima beans in each type of source listed below. Write the information you find in your Learning Log, and then use the lines below to begin writing a bibliography. Be sure to use the correct format for each type of source.

Book: **Possible Answer** Greene, Robert. Beans, Beans, and More Beans. Chicago:Showalter Publishing, 2005.

Encyclopedia: **Possible Answer** "The Life of a Lima Bean." Encyclopedia of Crops and Agriculture. 2002 ed.

Internet site: **Possible Answer** "Growing a Better Bean." The World's Most Nutritious Foods. November 29, 2006. The Farmer's Alliance for Healthy Nutrition. January 7, 2007. <http://www. farmersalliance.org/nutritiousfoods/limabeans.html>

## Revising

Use this checklist to revise the report of your experiment.

☐ Is your hypothesis clearly stated?

☐ Do your observations and research support the advice you provide?

☐ Have you included enough information from your Learning Log notes and clearly organized them?

☐ Have you cited all your sources in a bibliography?

## Editing/Proofreading

Use this checklist to correct mistakes.

☐ Have you used the proper format for each type of source in your bibliography?

☐ Did you check all capitalization, punctuation, and spelling?

☐ Have you read your report more than once to check for correctly used conjunctions throughout your almanac?

☐ Did you review any suspicious information and double-check your facts?

## Publishing

Use this checklist to publish your results.

☐ Rewrite your report neatly, or type it on a computer.

☐ Add graphs, charts, or other helpful illustrations to your report.

☐ Share your report with your teacher or a classmate.

Name _____     Date _____

# Spelling

**Focus**
- The prefix **ir-** means "not".
- The prefix **dis-** has several meanings: "opposite or lack of or not."
- **Root words** were formed from words of other languages, such as Greek and Latin. Here are some roots in the spelling words and their meanings:

  **port** = carry; **sign** = mark

**Practice** **Write the spelling word which is formed by adding the prefix *ir-* or *dis-* to each of the word parts.**

1. ir + reparable = _irreparable_
2. ir + refutable = _irrefutable_
3. dis + appearing = _disappearing_
4. dis + interest = _disinterest_

**Fill in the root word and write the resulting spelling word on the line.**

**sign**

5. _sign_ ature     signature
6. _sign_           sign

**port**

7. _port_ able      portable

**stella**

8. _stella_ r       stellar

**Word List**
1. discouraged
2. irregular
3. portable
4. import
5. displace
6. irrelevant
7. sign
8. signify
9. disembark
10. signal
11. exporting
12. national
13. irrefutable
14. porter
15. transportation
16. disinterest
17. signature
18. insignia
19. irrational
20. irreparable

**Apply** Fill in the blanks with the appropriate letters to create a spelling word from the list and write it on the line.

9. p__ort____able = _portable_

10. __ir_____regular = _irregular_

11. __dis____embark = _disembark_

12. s__ign____al = _signal_

13. __ir_____relevant = _irrelevant_

14. in__sign___ia = _insignia_

15. __dis____appearing = _disappearing_

16. p__ort____er = _porter_

17. trans__port___ation = _transportation_

18. s__ig____n = _sign_

19. ex__port___ing = _exporting_

20. im__port___ = _import_

21. __dis____couraged = _discouraged_

22. __ir_____refutable = _irrefutable_

23. __sign___ature = _signature_

24. __ir_____reparable = _irreparable_

25. __sign___ify = _signify_

26. __dis____place = _displace_

27. __dis____interest = _disinterest_

28. __ir_____rational = _irrational_

Name _____ Date _____

# Electronic Technology: Retrieving and Reviewing Information

**Focus**

- Searching for and retrieving information is much easier because of **electronic technology.** The Internet, online encyclopedias, and electronic library catalogs provide quick access to large amounts of information. Knowing how to choose **keywords** for your searches is an important skill in using electronic technology.

- Electronic technology also helps you review the things you have written. **Word-processing programs** can check for errors in spelling and grammar. They will not catch every error, however; you must still proofread your work. For example, homophones and homographs are often overlooked by word-processing programs.

**Practice** A word-processing program corrected most of the errors in the paragraph below. However, there are four errors it did not catch. Read the paragraph carefully, and circle the errors.

Thomas Edison was borne in 1847 in Milan, Ohio. During his teen years, Edison worked several odd jobs before becoming a telegraph operator. His fist inventions used telegraph technology to send information like stock numbers and vote tallies. Edison became a household name with his invention off the phonograph in 1877. People were amazed to here voices coming from a machine.

**Explain why the word-processing program may have missed these errors.**

**Possible Answers** *Borne* and *here* are homophones. The other words are words that resemble the intended words.

**Apply** Read the research topics below. Write at least two keywords you would use to begin a search for information about each topic.

**1.** How do birds know when to migrate?

**Possible Answers** birds, migration

**2.** What are the words in Abraham Lincoln's Gettysburg Address?

**Possible Answers** Lincoln, Gettysburg, Civil War

**3.** How does milk get from a cow to your refrigerator?

**Possible Answers** milk, dairy, farm, transportation

**4.** Where is the tallest tree in the world located?

**Possible Answers** tallest, tree

**5.** Who wrote *The Decline and Fall of the Roman Empire?*

**Possible Answers** author, Roman, Empire, Decline

**6.** Who is the current president of Angola?

**Possible Answers** Angola, president

**7.** Which ocean is the largest?

**Possible Answers** ocean, largest

**8.** What is the function of your kidneys?

**Possible Answers** kidneys, function

Name _____     Date _____

# Inflectional Ending *-ed*

- Adding the **inflectional ending *-ed*** to a verb creates the past tense of the verb.

  They **work** from dawn to dusk.
  They **worked** from dawn to dusk.

- Verbs that end with the inflectional ending *-ed* can also form the past participle. This verb form can be used as a verb or an adjective.

  That **baked** apple smells great!

**Practice**   **Rewrite the following sentences so that they are in the past tense.**

1. The astronauts land their spaceship on another planet.

   The astronauts landed their spaceship on another planet.

2. My friends and I dine in the cafeteria.

   My friends and I dined in the cafeteria.

3. The horses carry the riders along the trail.

   The horses carried the riders along the trail.

4. The workers rip long strips of wallpaper off the wall.

   The workers ripped long strips of wallpaper off the wall.

5. I type my research paper on the computer.

   I typed my research paper on the computer.

6. My calves itch where they touched poison ivy.

   My calves itched where they touched poison ivy.

**Apply**

**A word ending in -ed has been boldfaced in each sentence below. On the line, write V if the word is used as a verb, or A if it is an adjective.**

7. ____V____ A motorcycle **zipped** past us on the freeway.

8. ____A____ For dessert, Ms. Christo usually eats **canned** peaches sprinkled with sugar.

9. ____A____ Amy's **knotted** hair took half an hour to untangle.

10. ____V____ I **switched** places with Jasmine in social studies.

11. ____A____ I looked closely at the **graded** tests.

12. ____A____ Luiz and his uncle drank **iced** tea on the porch.

13. ____V____ The nurse **checked** on the patients in his care.

14. ____V____ We **shredded** cheese to spread on the pizza.

Name _____ Date _____

# Selection Vocabulary

**Focus**

**electromagnets** (i • lek' • trō • mag' • nits) *n.* plural of **electromagnet:** a piece of iron with wire wound around it. It becomes a magnet when an electric current is passed through the wire. (page 170)

**squinted** (skwint' • əd) *v.* past tense of **squint:** to partially close the eyes (page 173)

**observe** (əb • zûrv') *v.* to make a careful study of (page 174)

**crane** (krān) *n.* a large machine with a long arm that can be moved up and down and in a circle. Cables at the end of the crane's arm are used to lift and move heavy objects. (page 174)

**hypothesis** (hī • poth' • i • sis) *n.* something that is suggested as being true for the purposes of further investigation (page 175)

**munchkin** (munch' • kin) *n.* a very small person (page 177)

**positive** (po' • zi • tiv) *adj.* having one of two opposite kinds of electric charge (page 179)

**negative** (neg' • ə • tiv) *adj.* having one of two opposite kinds of electric charge (page 179)

**practically** (prak' • tik • lē) *adv.* nearly; almost (page 181)

**conclusions** (kən • klōō' • zhəns) *n.* plural of **conclusion:** something decided after thinking and experimenting (page 181)

**Practice** Write the vocabulary word on the line that best completes each sentence.

1. The scientist's experiments proved that his __hypothesis__ was correct.

2. Electricity contains both __negative__ and positive charges.

3. My mom called me "__munchkin__" when I was a little baby.

4. __Observe__ closely how the magician makes the cards disappear.

5. The giant crane uses _electromagnets_ to lift heavy objects.

6. A negative charge is attracted to a _positive_ charge.

7. The builders used a _crane_ to lift steel beams onto the roof.

8. After leaving the dark theater, I _squinted_ because of the bright sunlight.

9. Dr. Wong and Dr. Shepherd drew different _conclusions_ from the X-rays.

10. We had _practically_ finished building the model when my dog sat on it.

**Apply**   Write *C* in the blank if the selection vocabulary word has been defined correctly. Write *I* in the blank if it has been defined incorrectly, and write the correct word on the line.

11. *Positive* means "something that is suggested as being true for the purposes of an investigation."

    ___I___   hypothesis

12. To *observe* means "to make a careful study of."

    ___C___   _____

13. *Conclusions* are things decided after thinking and experimenting.

    ___C___   _____

14. *Cranes* are pieces of iron wrapped in wire with electric currents running through them.

    ___I___   electromagnets

**Name** _____ **Date** _____

# Making Conjectures

Our question or problem:
**Possible Answer** Why is it important to conserve energy?

_____

_____

_____

Conjecture (my first theory or explanation):
**Possible Answer** I think it is important to conserve energy because some forms of energy are not renewable.

_____

_____

As you collect information, your conjecture will change. Return to this page to record your new theories or explanations about your question or problem.

# Establishing Investigation Needs

My group's question or problem:
**Possible Answer** Why is it important to conserve energy?

**Knowledge Needs**—Information I need to find or figure out in order to investigate the question or problem:

A. **Possible Answer** Why is it important to conserve energy?

B. _____

C. _____

D. _____

E. _____

| Source | Useful? | How? |
|---|---|---|
| Encyclopedias | | |
| Books | yes | about energy use and history |
| Magazines | yes | articles about energy conservation |
| Newspapers | | |
| Video and Audio Clips | yes | programs on energy conservation |
| Television | | |
| Interviews, observations | | |
| Museums | | |
| Other | yes | to collect information on solar and wind power |

Inquiry • *Skills Practice 1*

Name _____ Date _____

# Book Review

**Think**

**Audience: Who** will read your book review?

**Possible Answer** someone interested in this book

**Purpose: What** do you want your book review to do?

**Possible Answer** I want to convince other people to read this story.

**Prewriting**

**A book review should summarize the plot, describe the characters, and offer an opinion about the book. Use this graphic organizer to help plan your book review.**

| | |
|---|---|
| **Title** | **Possible Answer** *Roll of Thunder, Hear My Cry* by Mildred D. Taylor |
| **Author's Purpose** | **Possible Answer** to entertain |
| **Summary** | **Possible Answer** The Logans are an African American family living in the South in the 1930s. Cassie Logan, the main character, is nine. She learns about racism and its effects. She also finds out why her family's land is so important. |
| **Your Opinions** | **Possible Answer** I thought this was an interesting book. The characters were very realistic, and I felt like I knew them by the end. The book deals with tough issues but leaves you feeling hopeful. |
| **Your Recommendation** | **Possible Answer** I recommend this book to anyone who likes an exciting plot and strong characters. |

## Revising Use this checklist to revise your book review.

☐ Did you include an introduction that gives the basic facts about your book, such as title and author?

☐ Have you described the major characters or people who appear in the book?

☐ Does your summary give the reader a clear idea of the plot?

☐ Have you clearly stated your recommendations and opinions about the book?

☐ Have you written a bibliography for the sources you used to create your book review? Are your paragraphs clear and cogent?

## Editing/Proofreading Use this checklist to correct mistakes.

☐ Did you spell the title and author's name correctly?

☐ Do your nouns and pronouns agree?

☐ Did you check for spelling errors, including those errors missed by a spell-checker?

## Publishing Use this checklist to prepare for publication.

☐ Rewrite your book review neatly, or type it on a computer.

☐ Share your book review with the class by reading it aloud.

**Name** _____  **Date** _____

# Spelling

**Focus**

- When you add the **inflectional ending -ed** to a verb, it forms the past tense of that verb. Drop the e if a word ends in e. If a word is more than one syllable and ends in -er, do not change the spelling of the base word if the last syllable is not accented. If the word ends in a short vowel followed by a single consonant, then double the consonant.

- The prefix **il-** means "not," and is added to words that begin with l.

- **Synonyms** are words with the same, or nearly the same, meaning. A word may have many synonyms that have slightly different meanings.

**Word List**
1. pictured
2. illiterate
3. laminated
4. registered
5. supposed
6. featured
7. uproar
8. tumult
9. extraordinary
10. pandemonium
11. illegible
12. illegal
13. selected
14. wonderful
15. inflamed
16. illogical
17. marvelous
18. consistent
19. hindered
20. complimented

**Practice** Add the prefix il- or the inflectional ending -ed to the following base words to form spelling words from the list. Write the words on the lines.

1. picture    pictured
2. suppose    supposed
3. logical    illogical
4. legal    illegal
5. literate    illiterate
6. laminate    laminated
7. legible    illegible
8. feature    featured
9. register    registered

## Spelling (cont.)

10. select    selected
11. inflame    inflamed
12. hinder    hindered
13. compliment    complimented

On the lines, write the spelling words from the list that are synonyms for the following words.

**disorder**

14. uproar
15. tumult
16. pandemonium

**fantastic**

17. extraordinary
18. wonderful
19. marvelous

**reliable**

20. consistent

**Apply**

On the line, write the spelling word from the list that is related by a common base or root word to each of the following words.

21. hinder    hindered
22. legal    illegal
23. picture    pictured
24. select    selected
25. inflame    inflamed
26. feature    featured
27. laminate    laminated
28. logical    illogical
29. compliment    complimented
30. legible    illegible

31. register    registered
32. literate    illiterate
33. suppose    supposed
34. roaring    uproar
35. consist    consistent
36. wondering    wonderful
37. tumultuous    tumult
38. ordinary    extraordinary
39. pandemic    pandemonium
40. marvel    marvelous

Name _____   Date _____

# Pronouns

**Focus**

- A **subject pronoun** replaces one or more nouns in the subject. *I, you, he, she, it, we,* and *they* are subject pronouns.

- An **object pronoun** replaces one or more nouns in the predicate. *Me, you, her, him, it, us,* and *them* are object pronouns.

- A **possessive pronoun** shows ownership. *My, your, her, his, our, your, its,* and *their* are used with nouns. *Mine, yours, hers, his, its, ours, yours,* and *theirs* are used alone.

- **They** organized a yard sale. **She** ran to first base.

- Ishiko came with **me** to the concert. Uncle Tito played with **them**. I gave **her** my notes.

- **Your** sister scored a goal. Therese can have **mine**. This last slice of pie is **yours**.

**Practice** Circle the pronouns in this paragraph.

On (our) way home from school, Aaron and (I) almost always stop at the little store about a block from (my) house. (He) buys a bottle of soda and nearly finishes (it) before (we) even get back outside. (I) do not like pop. (Its) flavor is too sugary for (me). (I) usually get a couple of apples, but (I) eat (them) slowly. (I) like knowing that (they) are a healthful snack.

**Apply** The sentences below contain misused pronouns. Rewrite each sentence so that it is correct.

**1.** Mine brother is studying for him college entrance exams.

My brother is studying for his college entrance exams.

_____

**2.** They's shirts got splattered with mud from we's driveway.

Their shirts got splattered with mud from our driveway.

_____

**3.** Us are joining you's class for a field trip to the museum.

We are joining your class for a field trip to the museum.

_____

**4.** Me have decided to invite thems to mine's favorite restaurant.

I have decided to invite them to my favorite restaurant.

_____

**5.** It high walls helped protect we from our's enemies.

Its high walls helped protect us from our enemies.

_____

**6.** Nina's dad drove she and me to our's dance lessons.

Nina's dad drove her and me to our dance lessons.

_____

**Name** _____  **Date** _____

# Comparatives, Superlatives, and the Prefix *re-*

**Focus**

- A **comparative adjective** or **adverb** compares one person, action, or thing to another.

- A **superlative adjective** or **adverb** compares one person, action, or thing to several others.

- When forming the **comparative**, most longer modifiers must be preceded by the word **more.**

- When forming the **superlative**, most longer modifiers must be preceded by the word **most.**

- The prefix **re-** means "again." For example, *reuse* means "to use again."

- I am **taller** now than I was two years ago.

- That is the **prettiest** painting in the museum.

- Tom was **more patient** than Jim.

- Of all the members of her track team, Kyra runs **most quickly.**

**Practice**  **Rewrite each sentence below so that it contains a word using the prefix *re-* and a comparative or superlative adjective or adverb.**

**Possible Answers**

**Example**  Emile had to wash the glasses again in the small sink.
Emile had to rewash the glasses in the smallest sink she had ever seen.

1. Suddenly, the rabbit appeared again in the lovely meadow.

   Suddenly, the rabbit reappeared in the loveliest meadow in the park.

2. The good ice cream shop will not open again until next summer.

   The best ice cream shop will not reopen until next summer.

**3.** I had to listen to LaTonya tell the pleasant story again.

_I had to listen to LaTonya retell the most pleasant story I had heard._

**4.** Julio discovered again a large science kit in his closet.

_Julio rediscovered the largest science kit in his closet._

**5.** Please state your answer again.

_Please restate your answer louder than before._

**Apply** **Write the comparative and superlative forms for each word.**

**6.** simple _simpler, simplest_

**7.** crowded _more or less crowded, most or least crowded_

**8.** straight _straighter, straightest_

**9.** likely _more or less likely, most or least likely_

**10.** early _earlier, earliest_

**11.** smooth _smoother, smoothest_

**12.** funny _funnier, funniest_

**13.** powerfully _more or less powerfully, most or least powerfully_

**14.** dangerously _more or less dangerously, most or least dangerously_

**15.** difficult _more or less difficult, most or least difficult_

Name _____  Date _____

# Selection Vocabulary

**Focus**

**flickering** (flic' • kər • ing) *adj.* burning or shining in an irregular way (page 190)

**expands** (ik • spandz') *v.* becomes larger (page 191)

**propel** (prə • pel') *v.* to cause to move forward (page 191)

**gusty** (gus' • tē) *adj.* blowing in strong, sudden bursts (page192)

**reliable** (ri • lī' • ə • bəl) *adj.* able to be depended on (page 192)

**revolving doors** (ri • vôl' • ving dors) *n.* plural of **revolving door:** a door at the front of the building that moves in a circle around a central point (page 193)

**converts** (kən • vûrts') *v.* changes into something different (page 194)

**currents** (kûr' • ənts) *n.* plural of **current:** a flow of electricity (page 194)

**fossil fuels** (fôs' • əl fyoō' • əls) *n.* plural of **fossil fuel:** a fuel formed from the remains of plants and animals. Coal and petroleum are fossil fuels. (page 195)

**economical** (ek' • ə • nôm' • i • kəl) *adj.* a good use of resources; not wasteful (page 195)

**Practice**  **Circle the word in parentheses that best fits each sentence.**

1. A solar panel (converts, currents) sunlight into electricity.

2. Please use the (fossil fuels, revolving doors) to enter the building.

3. The suitcase (converts, expands) to hold more clothing.

4. Using coupons and watching for sales are (economical, gusty) ways to shop.

5. Burning (currents, ~~fossil fuels~~) is probably not the best way to create energy.

6. This digital watch is much more (~~reliable~~, flickering) than my old one.

7. Electrical (revolving doors, ~~currents~~) will not flow through insulating materials.

8. Kicking your legs will help (converts, ~~propel~~) you through the water.

9. I knew the batteries were almost dead when the flashlight began (expands, ~~flickering~~).

10. A (reliable, ~~gusty~~) breeze threatened to capsize the sailboat.

**Apply**   Write the selection vocabulary word that best answers each question below.

11. Which word describes someone who always shows up on time and never goes back on his or her word? _____reliable_____

12. Which word describes what a balloon filling with air does? _____expands_____

13. Which word describes water moving in the ocean or electricity moving through a wire? _____currents_____

14. A banker changes French francs into American dollars. Which word describes what he does? _____converts_____

15. A drooping flag suddenly lifts in a strong breeze. Just as quickly, it droops back down. What kind of wind is blowing? _____gusty_____

Name _____   Date _____

# Cause and Effect

**Focus** When one event causes another to happen, the events have a **cause-and-effect relationship.**

- A **cause** is the reason that an event happens.
- An **effect** is the result of a cause.
- Writers use words such as *because, since, therefore,* and *so* to show the reader that a cause-and-effect relationship has taken place.

**Practice** On a separate piece of paper, answer the following questions about causes and effects in the story "The Wind at Work."

1. What caused the Dutch to build windmills throughout the flatlands?
   **Possible Answer** The land was often flooded by the sea.
2. How did harnessing the wind for power affect working conditions? **Possible Answer** People and animals did not have to work nearly as hard.
3. What caused windmills to become less widely used?
   **Possible Answer** Steam power and gas engines were invented.
4. What effect would using more wind power have on the environment?
   **Possible Answer** There would be less pollution.
5. What caused humans to begin relying so heavily on fossil fuels?
   **Possible Answer** Fossil fuels were more reliable.

**Apply**   One-half of each cause-and-effect relationship is missing in the sentences below. Complete the sentences by providing the missing half.

6. When my alarm rang this morning, **Possible Answer** I hopped out of bed and jumped in the shower.

7. Highway 56 is closed; therefore, **Possible Answer** traffic will need to take a detour.

8. Since Annika is bringing a dessert to the party, **Possible Answer** I should bring something to drink.

9. Tucker raised his hand because **Possible Answer** he knew the answer.

10. People are not allowed to skateboard there, so **Possible Answer** I usually go to McReynolds Skate Park.

11. The entire class began laughing when **Possible Answer** the teacher told a joke.

12. Because my grandparents are visiting this weekend, **Possible Answer** we are cleaning the apartment.

Name _____ Date _____

# Persuasive Letter

**Think**

**Audience: Who** will read your persuasive letter?

**Possible Answer** the principal

**Purpose: What** is your reason for writing a persuasive letter?

**Possible Answer** I want to start a recycling program at our school.

**Prewriting**

**Persuasive writing is used to convince someone to agree with your opinion. Use the graphic organizer below to plan your persuasive letter.**

| | |
|---|---|
| 1. Write your viewpoint (main idea). | **Possible Answer** Our school should have a recycling program. |
| 2. Provide facts, examples, and/or expert opinions that support the viewpoint presented. | **Possible Answer** Right now, all of our school's waste goes to a landfill where it will stay forever. At least half that waste is paper, glass, or metals that can be recycled. Harris Recycling will come get our recyclable waste for less than the garbage company charges. As an incentive, we can give prizes to the classrooms or grades that recycle the biggest percentage of their waste. |
| 3. In addition to providing hard facts, use an emotional appeal that you believe will be effective with the audience. | **Possible Answer** We cannot waste precious resources, or there will not be any left when we become adults. |
| 4. End your letter with a conclusion that restates the viewpoint or solution and asks the reader for action, if appropriate. | **Possible Answer** A recycling program is one of the most efficient ways our school can help the environment. |

## Revising

**Use this checklist to revise your persuasive letter.**

☐ Did you use formal language in your letter and include information that is appropriate for the audience?

☐ Does your letter have clear organization?

☐ Did you use persausive techniques, like emotional appeal, to convince your reader?

☐ Did you avoid using contractions and slang terms?

## Editing/Proofreading

**Use this checklist to correct mistakes.**

☐ Did you follow the correct format for a formal letter?

☐ Did you check all capitalization, punctuation, and spelling?

☐ Have you correctly used compound sentences?

☐ Have you correctly used subjective, objective, and possessive pronouns?

## Publishing

**Use this checklist to publish your persuasive letter.**

☐ Write your letter on a clean sheet of paper, or type your letter on a computer and print it.

☐ Address your envelope, and prepare your letter for sending.

**Name** _____    **Date** _____

# Spelling

**Focus**
- Understanding and identifying **Greek roots** and their meanings can help you define and spell difficult and unfamiliar words. Here are some of the Greek roots in the spelling words and their meanings:

*meter* = measure; *chron* = time; *therm* = heat

**Practice** Write the spelling word that results when the prefix *re-* is added.

1. apply         reapply
2. organize      reorganize
3. furnish       refurnish
4. purchase      repurchase
5. formulate     reformulate
6. introduce     reintroduce
7. affirm        reaffirm
8. inforce       reinforce
9. visit         revisit
10. generate     regenerate

**Word List**

1. refurnish
2. meter
3. diameter
4. reorganize
5. reintroduce
6. revisit
7. chronic
8. chronicle
9. reaffirm
10. barometer
11. reinforce
12. thermometer
13. reformulate
14. synchronize
15. repurchase
16. chronology
17. regenerate
18. centimeter
19. chronological
20. reapply

**Each of the following examples includes at least one Greek root. On the line, write the spelling word that is represented in each of the examples.**

11. chron + ological =    chronological
12. syn + chron + ize =    synchronize

13. therm + o + meter = <u>thermometer</u>
14. chron + ology = <u>chronology</u>
15. baro + meter = <u>barometer</u>
16. centi + meter = <u>centimeter</u>
17. chron + ic = <u>chronic</u>
18. dia + meter = <u>diameter</u>
19. chron + icle = <u>chronicle</u>

**Which Greek root in the spelling list is a word by itself?**

20. <u>meter</u>

**Apply** Decide which Greek root, when added, correctly spells the word in each sentence. Write the spelling word on the line.

21. A <u>therm</u>ometer measures heat.          <u>thermometer</u>
22. My little sister is almost one <u>meter</u> tall.     <u>meter</u>
23. The textbook listed the <u>chron</u>ology of events.  <u>chronology</u>
24. She suffers from <u>chron</u>ic pain.          <u>chronic</u>
25. Let's syn<u>chron</u>ize our watches.         <u>synchronize</u>

**On the line, write the spelling word that is related by a common base or root word to each of the following words.**

26. furnished        <u>refurnish</u>
27. purchasing       <u>repurchase</u>
28. application       <u>reapply</u>
29. formula          <u>reformulate</u>
30. introduction      <u>reintroduce</u>

Name _____ Date _____

# Regular and Irregular Plurals

**Focus** **Most regular plurals** are formed by just adding -s or -es, but **irregular plurals** do not follow any rules for forming the plural.

- For words that end in a consonant and *y*, change the *y* to *i* and then add -es.

- baby, babies
  fly, flies

- For some words that end in *f* or *fe*, change the *f* or *fe* to *v* and add -es.

- loaf, loaves
  shelf, shelves

- For words that end in a consonant and *o*, add either -s or -es. You must use a dictionary to determine which is correct.

- mango, mangos
  potato, potatoes
  rhino, rhinos

- For some words, the plural form is a different word.

- tooth, teeth
  child, children

- For some words, the singular and plural forms are the same.

- deer, deer
  fish, fish

**Practice** **For each singular word below, write its plural form on the line.**

1. floor _____ floors _____
2. bench _____ benches _____
3. candy _____ candies _____
4. loaf _____ loaves _____
5. deer _____ deer _____

6. journey _____ journeys _____
7. boss _____ bosses _____
8. tooth _____ teeth _____
9. hero _____ heroes _____
10. cliff _____ cliffs _____

**Apply** Complete each sentence below by writing the plural form of the word in parentheses on the line. Use a dictionary to check your answers.

11. My _____ friends _____ helped me rake leaves out of the garden. (friend)

12. How many _____ fish _____ are in the zoo's aquarium? (fish)

13. Dr. Lynn bought _____ tomatoes _____ and cucumbers at the market. (tomato)

14. Anna undid the _____ latches _____ on her suitcase. (latch)

15. They will travel through the mountains and _____ valleys _____ of Montana. (valley)

16. Several _____ mice _____ found a way into the pantry. (mouse)

17. We keep the butter _____ knives _____ in that top drawer. (knife)

18. Can you name all the _____ countries _____ in Africa? (country)

19. Three _____ people _____ waited in line in front of me at the deli. (person)

20. The students' _____ faces _____ lit up when they heard the news. (face)

21. One night a week, the Alis enjoy watching _____ videos _____ together. (video)

22. This book describes the _____ lives _____ of a few famous inventors. (life)

Name _____ Date _____

# Words with Latin Roots and the Prefix *non-*

- Many words in the English language contain **Latin roots.** For example, *portable, import,* and *porter* all contain the Latin root *port,* which means "to carry." Identifying and understanding Latin roots can help you define difficult words.

- The prefix **non-** means "not." When combined with a base or root word it forms an antonym of that word.

**Practice**  Each word below uses the prefix *non-* and contains a root word. On the line, write the word's definition. As a hint, you have been provided the meaning of each root word. Use a dictionary if you need help.

1. The Latin root *form* means "shape"

   *nonconform* = to not give the same shape

2. The Latin root *aqua* means "water"

   *nonaquatic* = not taking place in water

3. The Greek root *bio* means "life"

   *nonbiological* = not of or related to living things

4. The Latin root *sens* means "feel"

   *nonsensitive* = not easily affected by perception

**Apply**

**Each group of words uses the same Latin root. Select the correct meaning of the root word from the box, and write it on the line. Write an original sentence using each word.**

| ray | cut | different | hold |
|-----|-----|-----------|------|

**5.** variety; variable; various

Latin root *var* means <u>different</u>

**Possible Answer** <u>Through various speeches to the crew the</u> <u>captain let everyone know that on this ship he was in charge.</u>

**6.** radiator; radiation; radio

Latin root *rad* means <u>ray</u>

**Possible Answer** <u>Radio waves are present in the skies.</u>

**7.** dissect; intersect; section

Latin root *sect* means <u>cut</u>

**Possible Answer** <u>Omnivores and carnivores often intersect in</u> <u>a food chain.</u>

**8.** contain; maintain; detain

Latin root *tain* means <u>hold</u>

**Possible Answer** <u>The man was unable to maintain the pace</u> <u>of the race.</u>

Name _____  Date _____

# Selection Vocabulary

**Focus**

**food chain** (fōōd chān) *n.* a group of living things that form a chain in which the first living thing is eaten by the second, the second is eaten by the third, and so on (page 204)

**food web** (fōōd web) *n.* a group of food chains in an ecosystem that are connected (page 204)

**ecosystem** (ē' • kō • sis' • təm) *n.* all the living and nonliving things in a certain area (page 204)

**absorbs** (əb • sorbs) *v.* takes in (page 205)

**algae** (al' • jē) *n.* simple living things that are composed of one or more cells; most algae are plants that do not have roots or flowers. (page 208)

**ridges** (ri' • jez) *n.* plural of **ridge:** a raised, narrow strip (page 209)

**predators** (pre' • də • tərs) *n.* plural of **predator:** an animal that hunts and kills other animals for food (page 211)

**scavenger** (ska' • vən • jər) *n.* an animal that feeds on dead animals (page 211)

**omnivores** (om' • nə • vors') *n.* plural of **omnivore:** an animal that eats both animal flesh and plants (page 212)

**diet** (dī' • it) *n.* the food and drink eaten by an animal (page 212)

**Practice** If the boldfaced definition given for the underlined word in each sentence is correct, write *T* on the line. If the definition is incorrect, write *F* on the line.

**1.** The mouse scurried quickly through the field, hoping to avoid <u>predators</u>.

**animals that hunt other animals for food** _____T_____

**2.** The pool had not been used in years, so <u>algae</u> covered much of the water's surface.

**a kind of tarp or blanket** _____F_____

**3.** A horse's <u>diet</u> consists mainly of roughage and water.

**food and drink eaten by an animal** _____T_____

**4.** As we came around the bend, we startled a <u>scavenger</u> that had been eating.

**an animal that feeds on dead animals** _____T_____

**5.** Dr. Meredith studied the <u>food chain</u> in Lake Superior.

**the different things an animal will eat** _____F_____

**6.** A kitchen sponge <u>absorbs</u> water, but it also breeds bacteria.

**cleans or wipes** _____F_____

**7.** The desert <u>ecosystem</u> is more diverse than you might imagine.

**all the living and nonliving things in an area** _____T_____

**8.** At times, <u>omnivores</u> become predators.

**animals that eat both flesh and plants** _____T_____

**9.** Gum got embedded between the <u>ridges</u> on the bottom of my shoe.

**raised, narrow strips** _____T_____

**10.** A rain forest's <u>food web</u> contains many thousands of creatures.

**a method animals use to get their food** _____F_____

**Apply** Review the selection vocabulary words for "What Are Food Chains and Webs?". On a separate sheet of paper, write five sentences using at least two vocabulary words from this lesson in each sentence.

Name _____  Date _____

# Classify and Categorize

**Focus** Classifying and categorizing are ways of organizing information. They can help you better understand and remember what you read.

- **Classifying** is identifying the similarities that objects, characters, or events have in common with each other, and then grouping them by their similarities.

- **Categorizing** is the act of organizing the objects, characters, or events into groups, or categories.

**Practice** Reread pages 210–212 in "What Are Food Chains and Webs?". Animals that eat other animals can be categorized in several different ways. On the lines below, list the seven possible categories the text mentions for animals that eat other animals.

1. carnivores
2. secondary consumers
3. tertiary consumers
4. predators
5. scavengers
6. omnivores
7. opportunistic feeders

**Apply** Scientific classification is used around the world to classify plants, animals, and other organisms. Every living thing on Earth can be categorized into several groups that range from the very general to the very specific—from kingdoms to species. Classify the animals listed in the box by placing them into their appropriate categories in the chart below.

| chimpanzee | turtle | mouse | alligator | fruit fly |
| ladybug | cobra | horse | praying mantis | |

| Kingdom: Animalia | Class: Mammalia (Mammals) | chimpanzee |
| | | mouse |
| | | horse |
| | Class: Reptilia (Reptiles) | turtle |
| | | alligator |
| | | cobra |
| | Class: Insecta (Insects) | fruit fly |
| | | ladybug |
| | | praying mantis |

Comprehension Skill • *Skills Practice 1*

Name _____ Date _____

# Persuasive Report

**Think**

**Audience: Who** will read your persuasive report?
**Possible Answer** the school board

**Purpose: What** is your reason for writing a persuasive report?
**Possible Answer** I want to convince my school
district to use vegetable oil as fuel for its buses.

**Prewriting** The graphic organizer below will help you outline your persuasive report. Use the numbered lines to provide supporting facts and details for each subtopic. **Possible Answers**

**Topic:** Our school buses should run on vegetable oil.

**Subtopic:** Gasoline is expensive.

1. Gasoline prices continue to rise.
2. Gasoline might be running out soon.

**Subtopic:** Gasoline is not clean.

1. Fossil fuels cause pollution when they are burned.
2. Our buses use diesel gas, which is even dirtier than regular gasoline.

**Subtopic:** Used vegetable oil is readily available.

1. Fast food restaurants produce a lot of vegetable oil.
2. Used vegetable oil is free or very inexpensive.

**Subtopic:** We do not need to buy completely new school buses.

1. The buses' engines need to be modified.
2. The savings would make up for the initial costs.

**Conclusion:** Our school would set an example by using clean, inexpensive vegetable oil as a fuel.

## Revising

**Use this checklist to revise the draft of your report.**

☐ Is your draft organized according to the outline you prepared?

☐ Are your paragraphs cogent?

☐ Have you included facts and details that support and address your opinion?

☐ Do you have strong opening and concluding paragraphs?

☐ Did you use persuasive techniques to convince your reader?

## Editing/Proofreading

**Use this checklist to correct mistakes.**

☐ Have you correctly capitalized proper nouns?

☐ Have you spelled specialized words correctly and consistently throughout your report?

☐ Did you avoid using contractions and slang terms?

## Publishing

**Use this checklist to share your draft.**

☐ Neatly type your persuasive report and put it in your Writing Portfolio.

☐ Read the draft of your report to a group of classmates.

Name _____ Date _____

# Spelling

**Focus**

- Many words feature the prefix **non-**, which usually means "not." It often changes a base word to an antonym.
- Here are some of the **Latin roots** in the spelling words and their meanings:

  **sect** = cut; **vor** = eat; **carn** = meat; **herb** = "plant"; **jur, jud, jus** = "law"; **omni** = "all"

**Practice** Remove the prefix *non-* from each word and write the resulting word.

1. nonabrasive **abrasive**
2. nonconforming **conforming**
3. noncreative **creative**
4. nonsense **sense**
5. nonstick **stick**

**Fill in the appropriate Latin root or Latin root form and write the resulting spelling word on the line.**

6. **sect**ion **section**
7. **jur**isdiction **jurisdiction**
8. de**vour** **devour**
9. **jur**y **jury**
10. carni**vor**e **carnivore**

**Word List**

1. devour
2. nonviolent
3. section
4. nontoxic
5. nonstick
6. jury
7. nonessential
8. carnivore
9. herbivore
10. nonresident
11. dissect
12. intersect
13. noncreative
14. jurist
15. jurisdiction
16. nonsense
17. nonconforming
18. omnivore
19. nonprofit
20. nonabrasive

**Apply** | **Write the spelling word that matches each definition on the line.**

11. not fierce      <u>nonviolent</u>
12. not important      <u>nonessential</u>
13. not inventive      <u>noncreative</u>
14. not a member of a city      <u>nonresident</u>
15. not sticky      <u>nonstick</u>
16. not fitting in      <u>nonconforming</u>
17. not taking in gains      <u>nonprofit</u>
18. not rough      <u>nonabrasive</u>
19. not poisonous      <u>nontoxic</u>
20. not having meaning      <u>nonsense</u>

**Determine which Latin root correctly completes the word in each sentence. Write the appropriate Latin root and write the resulting spelling word on the lines below.**

21. A <u>jur</u>y judges whether a person is guilty or innocent.      <u>jury</u>

22. A <u>carn</u>ivore eats meat.      <u>carnivore</u>

23. The two streets inter<u>sect</u> by the gas station.      <u>intersect</u>

24. The <u>jur</u>ist did not know if the defendant was guilty.      <u>jurist</u>

25. That <u>sect</u>ion of the library holds fiction books.      <u>section</u>

26. The snake wanted to de<u>vour</u> the mouse.      <u>devour</u>

27. A giraffe is a herbi<u>vore</u>.      <u>herbivore</u>

28. The biologist began to dis<u>sect</u> the frog.      <u>dissect</u>

29. I am an <u>omni</u>vore.      <u>omnivore</u>

30. Which police station has <u>juris</u>diction over our neighborhood?      <u>jurisdiction</u>

Name _____  Date _____

# Possessive Nouns, Possessive Pronouns, and Conjunctions

**Focus**  **Possessive nouns and pronouns** show ownership.

- Add *'s* to singular nouns and plural nouns that do not end with *s* to form possessives.

- the pie**'s** flavor
  Chris**'s** textbook
  the children**'s** coats

- Add only an apostrophe to plural nouns that end with *s* to form possessives.

- students' answers
  cities' laws

- Possessive pronouns do not need apostrophes. They can be used in front of nouns or by themselves.

- **His** bicycle tire needs air.
  Where is **our** new classroom?
  This pencil is **yours.**

- A **conjunction** is a word that connects words or groups of words. A coordinating conjunction joins words or groups of words that are equally important in a sentence: *and, but, or, so, nor, either, yet,* and *for.*

- **Subordinating conjunctions** connect two clauses where one clause is grammatically dependent on the other: *after, although, before, if,* and *when.*

**Practice**  Circle the possessive noun or pronoun that correctly completes each sentence below and underline each conjunction.

1. Some of the trees are already beginning to lose (their, their's) leaves, before anyone predicted.

2. (Omars', Omar's) classmates voted for him to become student treasurer, although Jeremy was better in math.

3. Mrs. Riaz signed all her (employees', employee's) checks on the same day, and she never missed anyone.

4. (My, Mine) favorite actor has a new movie coming out soon, but it is not showing in my town.

5. The (runners's, runners') faces dripped with sweat, and they were exhausted.

**Apply** Use *and, but,* or *or* to complete each sentence below and circle each possessive noun and underline each possessive pronoun.

6. Next year I will have Ms. Patel for my math ___and___ social studies classes.

7. The Suarezes planned to take Nitesh's boat and go sailing, ___but___ there was hardly any wind.

8. You need to decide whether we will have pizza, ___or___ you will make your famous meatloaf.

9. Dana's soccer team will either score on this kick, ___or___ the game will be over.

10. A door slammed somewhere in the house, ___and___ then I heard my sister yelling.

11. Tulips, roses, ___and___ daisies are Faith's favorite flowers.

12. Mountain climbing is a thrilling activity, ___but___ you need professional training before you can use Tim's gear.

13. I want the Hawks to win in the finals, ___but___ the Bobcats are expected to win their third title.

14. Dante washed his face, brushed his teeth, ___and___ combed his hair before leaving the house.

**Name** _____ **Date** _____

# Irregular Verbs and the Prefix *mid-*

**Focus** The rule for forming the past tense of most verbs is to add *-ed.* **Irregular verbs** do not follow this rule. Instead you must learn the present tense, past tense, and past participle of each verb.

- For example, *run* and *ran* are different by only one letter, but *go* and *went* are completely different words.

- The prefix **mid-** means "at or in the middle of." For example, *midsection* means the section in the middle.

**Practice** Use the tense shown at the end of the sentence to decide which irregular verb correctly completes the sentence. Circle the correct choice. Underline the words in the sentences that contain the prefix *mid-.*

1. Most colonists (feel, (felt)) __felt__ strongly about their British rulers. **PAST**

2. In wartime it is often difficult to (found, (find)) __find__ normal, everyday items. **PRESENT**

3. Midway through the final quarter, he (leave, (left)) __left__ the football game to avoid traffic. **PAST**

4. He (come, (came)) __came__ at the midpoint of the conflict to give aid to the Patriots. **PAST**

5. I ((have,) had) __have__ never worked past midnight. **PRESENT**

**Apply** The following paragraphs contain incorrect past-tense verbs. On the line, write the correct past-tense form for each irregular verb.

Last summer my family and I **goed** _____went_____

to Philadelphia. When the trip **beginned** _____began_____

it was raining, but by the time we stopped for lunch, the sun

had **fighted** _____fought_____ its way through the clouds.

At Independence Hall the tour guide **telled**

_____told_____ us the story of the Declaration of

Independence. Afterward I **buyed** _____bought_____ a

postcard from the gift shop. I **writed** _____wrote_____

to my grandmother, telling her about everything we had seen

so far. My dad **thinked** _____thought_____ the postcard

was a thoughtful thing to do.

We **spended** _____spent_____ the next afternoon

watching a baseball game. The best part was when my

dad **catched** _____caught_____ a ball that was hit

into the stands. After we left the stadium, Dad **gived**

_____gave_____ it to my brother.

I **bringed** _____brought_____ my camera on the trip

and **taked** _____took_____ a lot of pictures. Sometime

I will show them to you.

Name _____     Date _____

# Selection Vocabulary

**Focus**

**colonies** (ko' • lə • nēz) *n.* plural of **colony:** a territory ruled by another country (page 288)

**loyal** (loi' • əl) *adj.* having or showing strong and lasting support for someone or something (page 289)

**settlers** (set' • lərz) *n.* plural of **settler:** a person who makes his or her home in a new land or country (page 291)

**protest** (prō' • test) *n.* to object to (page 292)

**liberty** (lib' • ər • tē) *n.* freedom from control of another country (page 294)

**militia** (mə • lish' • ə) *n.* a group of citizens trained to fight and help in emergencies (page 239)

**necessities** (nə • ses' • i • tēs) *n.* plural of **necessity:** something that is needed (page 299)

**pamphlets** (pam' • flitz) *n.* plural of **pamphlet:** a small book that has a paper cover (page 301)

**published** (pub' • lishd) *v.* past tense of **publish:** to print a newspaper, magazine, book, or other material and offer it for sale (page 301)

**discharge** (dis' • chärj) *n.* dismissal from service or a job (page 304)

**Practice**     **Write the selection vocabulary word that best fits each clue below.**

1. Dogs are often described with this word.

   Which word is it? _____loyal_____

2. When people do this, sometimes they make signs, gather in large groups, or sign petitions. What is it?

   _____protest_____

3. Many people fought very long and hard for this.

   What is it? _____liberty_____

**4.** This is a word used when someone is let go from a job.

Which word is it? _____ discharge _____

**5.** The United States was originally made of thirteen of these.

What are they? _____ colonies _____

**6.** This word describes water, clothing, and food.

Which word is it? _____ necessities _____

**7.** These could help you give information to other people.

What are they? _____ pamphlets _____

**8.** This group of people is trained to help others in an emergency.

Which word describes them? _____ militia _____

**9.** These people make their homes in new lands.

They are _____ settlers _____.

**10.** This word is the process of printing materials for sale to the public.

Which word is it? _____ published _____

**Apply**

**On a separate sheet of paper, challenge students to create five sentences using the selection vocabulary words. Each sentence should contain at least two vocabulary words. Make sure to use each word at least once.**

**Answers will vary.**

# Cause and Effect

**Focus**
When one event causes another to happen, the events have a **cause-and-effect relationship.**

- A cause is the reason that an event happens.

- An effect is the result of the cause.

- Writers use words such as *because, since, therefore,* and *so* to show the reader that a cause-and-effect relationship has taken place.

**Practice**
**Review the selection ". . . If You Lived at the Time of the American Revolution" to find out why the following events happened. Write down the cause for each event.**

**Possible Answers**

1. The Patriots dumped England's tea into Boston Harbor because

   they were angry about the taxes on tea_____.

2. The British soldiers were called Redcoats because

   their uniforms were red_____.

3. Many families were split because

   they had both Loyalist and Patriot family members_____.

4. Certain soldiers in the Continental Army were called minutemen because

   they could be ready for battle in a minute_____.

5. During the war, paper money lost value because

   too much of it was printed_____.

**Apply** The sentences below are incomplete. Each sentence shows only one half of a cause-and-effect relationship. At the beginning of each sentence, write *C* if you are given the cause. Write *E* if you are given the effect. Then, complete the sentence by adding the missing half.

6. __C__ The front tire of Reggie's bicycle was flat, so

**Possible Answer** he had to walk to school _____.

7. __E__ Monika grabbed an umbrella as she left home because

**Possible Answer** the weather forecast called for rain _____.

8. __C__ Since our soccer team won nearly all its games,

**Possible Answer** we will get to play in the finals _____.

9. __C__ Sophie has books due at the library; therefore

**Possible Answer** she needs to return them _____.

10. __E__ A section of our street is closed because

**Possible Answer** the city is working on the sewer _____.

**Now write your own cause-and-effect sentences using *therefore, since, because,* and *so.***

**Possible Answer** John missed the bus; therefore he was late for school.

**Possible Answer** Since Jose enjoyed American history, he did his report

on the Declaration of Independence.

**Possible Answer** Because it was raining, the baseball game was

cancelled.

**Possible Answer** Laura liked basketball, so she tried out for the basketball

team.

Name _____ Date _____

# Recording Concept Information

**As I read the selection, this is what I added to my understanding of the unit theme Making a New Nation.** Possible Answers

- ". . . If You Lived at the Time of the American Revolution" by Kay Moore

I learned that Americans made many sacrifices for freedom.

- "The Midnight Ride of Paul Revere" by Henry Wadsworth Longfellow

I learned that the poem is not historically accurate. However, the poem portrays the events in an inspired manner.

- "The Master Spy of Yorktown" by Burke Davis

I learned that African-American spies were key to helping defeat the British and securing America's independence.

- "Shh! We're Writing the Constitution" by Jean Fritz

I learned that the writing of the U.S. Constitution was a long and difficult process and there were several drafts.

- "Give Me Liberty!" by Russell Freedman I learned that the signers of the Declaration of Independence risked their lives by signing the document.

Name _____ Date _____

# Knowledge About Making a New Nation

- This is what I know about making a new nation before reading the unit.

**Possible Answer** America made itself into a new nation when it broke free of England. There were thirteen colonies which later became states. The Revolution was started in part because the colonies thought taxation without representation was unfair.

- These are some things about making a new nation that I would like to talk about and understand better.

**Possible Answer** What were the battles like during the American Revolution? Could a nation be formed without fighting? What makes our nation unique compared to other nations?

Reminder: I should read this page again when I get to the end of the unit to see how much my ideas about making a new nation have changed.

**Name** _____ **Date** _____

# Ideas About Making a New Nation

Of the ideas discussed in class about making a new nation, these are the ones I found most interesting.

**Possible Answer** Many different people took part in the American Revolution. The founders played their part, but many other lesser known individuals put equal amounts of effort into fulfilling the goal of independence.

_____

_____

_____

_____

_____

_____

_____

_____

_____

_____

_____

_____

## Ideas About Making a New Nation (continued)

**Write down the ideas you found most interesting about the selection ". . . If You Lived at the Time of the American Revolution." Discuss your ideas with the class.**

**Possible Answer** Many people made sacrifices during the American Revolution. Because of shortages and the loss of trade many common items were hard to obtain. Everyone who lived in the colonies was affected in one way or another.

Name _____ Date _____

# Timed Writing: Persuasive Writing

 **Think**

**Audience: Who** will read your persuasive writing?

**Possible Answer** the teacher
_____

**Purpose: Why** are you writing to persuade?

**Possible Answer** to convince my teacher that our lunch

break should be longer.

**Prewriting**

In school, you may be given only a short amount of time to write an essay or a paragraph. Your first step should always be to read the directions carefully. For the assignment below, circle the most important information in the directions. Then, list three ideas you might write about to complete the assignment.

Write a persuasive paragraph about a rule or law that you think is unfair. Be sure to include at least three sentences supporting your argument. Also include one sentence that tells the opposite point of view. You have twenty minutes to complete the paragraph.

1. **Possible Answers** Kids cannot drive until they are sixteen.
_____

2. **Possible Answers** Cell phones are not allowed in the classroom.
_____

3. **Possible Answers** A one-hour limit for using the library's computers.
_____

_____

## Revising    Use this checklist to revise your persuasive paragraph.

☐ Did you clearly state your opinion in the opening sentence?

☐ Did you include three sentences supporting your argument?

☐ Did you include one sentence about the opposite point of view?

☐ Did you use formal language?

## Editing/Proofreading    Use this checklist to correct mistakes.

☐ Are there any spelling errors?

☐ Have you used adjectives to modify nouns and pronouns?

☐ Do all the sentences contain correct punctuation?

☐ Have you corrected any contractions?

## Publishing    Use this checklist to prepare your persuasive paragraph for publication.

☐ If you have time, rewrite your paragraph neatly on a fresh sheet of paper.

☐ Hand in your completed Timed Writing assignment.

Name _____ Date _____

# Spelling

**Focus**

• When you add the inflectional ending **-ed** to a verb, it forms the past tense. Drop the e if a word ends in e, and then add the -ed ending. If the word ends in a short vowel followed by a single consonant, then double the consonant.

• **Irregular verbs** are verbs that do not form the past tense by adding -ed: *choose, chose; forbid, forbade; creep, crept.* Knowing the past tense of irregular verbs will help you prevent spelling mistakes.

• A prefix changes the meaning of the base word it precedes. Identifying prefixes and understanding their meanings can help you figure out the meaning and spelling of a difficult or unfamiliar word. The prefix **mid-** means "the middle." It does not change the spelling of the base word to which it is added.

**Word List**

1. midnight
2. chose
3. escaped
4. midyear
5. choose
6. downloaded
7. midsection
8. forbid
9. forbade
10. graduated
11. midterm
12. midstream
13. creep
14. crept
15. financed
16. communicated
17. midfield
18. midland
19. employed
20 midsummer

**Practice**

Add the inflectional ending **-ed** to the following base words and write the resulting spelling words on the lines.

1. download _____downloaded_____

2. employ _____employed_____

3. communicate _____communicated_____

4. graduate _____graduated_____

5. finance _____financed_____

6. escape _____escaped_____

Write the present tense and past tense of the irregular verbs in the spelling list. **Possible Answers**

| Present | Past |
|---------|------|
| 7. creep | crept |
| 8. choose | chose |
| 9. forbid | forbade |

Add the prefix *mid-* to the following base words and write the resulting spelling words on the lines.

10. land    midland
11. year    midyear
12. night    midnight
13. stream    midstream

14. field    midfield
15. summer    midsummer
16. section    midsection
17. term    midterm

 **Apply** If the underlined verb in the sentence is incorrect, write the correct form of the verb from the spelling list on the line. If it is correct, write correct.

18. Yesterday, I <u>forbidded</u> him to leave.    forbade

19. We <u>downloadded</u> that new game last week.    downloaded

20. We never <u>communicatted</u> very well.    communicated

21. The couple <u>financed</u> their car payment.    correct

22. The store <u>employed</u> ten people.    correct

23. The sisters <u>creppt</u> downstairs.    crept

24. The mouse <u>escapped</u> from the cat.    escaped

Name _____  Date _____

# Comparative and Superlative Adjectives and Adverbs

**Focus**

| Rule | Example |
|---|---|
| • A **comparative adjective** or **adverb** compares one person, thing, or action to another. | • I am **taller** now than I was two years ago. |
| • A **superlative adjective** or **adverb** compares one person, thing, or action to several others. | • That is the **prettiest** painting in the museum. |
| • For most longer modifiers use the word *more* for the comparative, or *most,* for the superlative instead of the *-er* or *-est* endings. | • Tom was **more patient** than Jim. Of all her team members, Kyra runs **most quickly.** |

**Practice** Write the comparative and superlative forms of each adjective and adverb listed below.

**1.** quiet  quieter, quietest

**2.** crispy  crispier, crispiest

**3.** hot  hotter, hottest

**4.** soon  sooner, soonest

**5.** excited  more or less excited, most or least excited

**6.** slowly  more or less slowly, most or least slowly

**7.** interesting  more or less interesting, most or least interesting

> **Apply** Cross out the incorrect form of each comparative or superlative adjective or adverb in each sentence. Then, write the correct form on the line that follows.

**8.** The three-toed sloth moves the ~~slowliest~~ of all

land mammals. _____ most slowly _____

**9.** The koala is ~~more fast~~ than the three-toed sloth, but only

when it is awake. _____ faster _____

**10.** Koalas spend about twenty-two hours a day sleeping,
making them the ~~more sleepy~~ of all of animals.

_____ sleepiest _____

**11.** The capybara, a rodent that can weigh more than one
hundred pounds, is definitely ~~heaviest~~ than an

average mouse. _____ heavier _____

**12.** The black mamba's speed and deadly bite make it the

world's ~~dangerest~~ snake. _____ most dangerous _____

**13.** At one hundred fifty years, the reptile that lives ~~most longly~~ is the Galapagos tortoise.

_____ longest _____

**14.** The world's ~~largerest~~ spider has a perfect name—the

Goliath birdeater. _____ largest _____

**15.** With a wingspan of thirteen feet, the Marabou stork has
the ~~most widest~~ wingspan of all birds.

_____ widest _____

**Name** _____ **Date** _____

# Homophones and the Suffix *-less*

**Focus**

**Homophones** are words that sound the same but have different spellings and meanings. The following word pairs are examples of homophones.

| there | for | would | so | made | wear |
|-------|-----|-------|-----|------|------|
| their | four | wood | sew | maid | where |

Many words feature the suffix *-less.* This suffix means "without" when added to base or root words.

Hope + less = without hope

Fear + less = without fear

**Practice** **Fill in the blank in each sentence with the appropriate homophone.**

| rose | rows | threw | through |
|------|------|-------|---------|

**1.** At the end of the school year, I gave a single red
_____rose_____ to my favorite teacher, Ms. Mendoza.

**2.** All the _____rows_____ were filled with people awaiting the performance.

**3.** The crowd cheered when the quarterback _____threw_____ a touchdown in the final seconds of the game.

**4.** The Millers will have to travel _____through_____ the mountains to reach their new home.

**Write the word on the line that corresponds with the definition.**

| baseless<br>powerless | tireless<br>seamless | careless<br>thoughtless |
|---|---|---|

5. Without seams or interruptions ___seamless___

6. Without thought ___thoughtless___

7. Without a care ___careless___

8. Without getting tired ___tireless___

9. Without a base or foundation for a thought ___baseless___

10. Identify the two base words that are also homophones. Provide the other half of the homophone pair.

seam, seem

base, bass

**Apply** **Each underlined word is part of a homophone group. Write another word from the homophone group on the line. Provide a matching homophone and then write a sentence using it correctly.**

Possible Answers

11. Then he said, "Good Night!" and with muffled oar

Silently <u>rowed</u> to the Charleston shore ___road or rode___

The road curved around the mountains.

12. A line of black that bends and floats

On the rising <u>tide</u>, like a bridge of boats. ___tied___

I tied a ribbon around the gift.

Word Structure • *Skills Practice 1*

Name _____ Date _____

# Selection Vocabulary

**Focus**

**aloft** (ə • lôft') *adv.* far above the ground (page 317)

**muffled** (muf • əld) *adj.* past tense of **muffle:** to wrap or cover to soften the sound or to protect (page 317)

**magnified** (mag • ni • fīd) *v.* past tense of **magnify:** to make something look bigger than it really is (page 317)

**mount** (mount) *v.* to get on (page 319)

**gleam** (glēm) *n.* a flash or beam of light (page 319)

**ledge** (lej) *n.* a narrow surface on a cliff or rock wall (page 321)

**sentinel** (sen' • tə • nəl) *n.* a sentry (page 260)

**weathercock** (weth • ər • kôk') *n.* a weathervane (page 322)

**assigned** (ə • sīnd') *v.* past tense of **assign:** to give out as a task (page 327)

**spread** (spred) *v.* to make or become known by more people (page 327)

**Practice**  Write the word from the word box that matches each definition below.

| gleam | mount | muffled | magnified | ledge |
|-------|-------|---------|-----------|-------|
| assigned | weathercock | aloft | spread | sentinel |

1. _____gleam_____ a flash or beam of light

2. _____magnified_____ made something look bigger than it really is

3. _____aloft_____ far above the ground

4. _____spread_____ to make or become known by more people

5. _____ledge_____ a narrow surface on a cliff or rock wall

6. _**sentinel**_ a sentry

7. _**mount**_ to get on

8. _**assigned**_ gave out as a task

9. _**weathercock**_ a weathervane

10. _**muffled**_ wrapped or covered to soften the sound or to protect

**Apply** Circle the word in parentheses that best fits each sentence.

11. Allison (**muffled**/assigned) the alarm clock, but we still heard it.

12. Michael slowly crawled across the snowy (**ledge**/weathercock).

13. The balloon was held (**aloft**/honorable) by the wind.

14. The news will (**spread**/mount) quickly to the rest of the family.

15. Let's (witness/**mount**) our horses and ride through the meadow.

16. The (**gleam**/ledge) of the car blinded me.

Vocabulary • *Skills Practice 1*

Name _____     Date _____

# Formulating Questions and Problems

A good question or problem to investigate:

**Possible Answer** If I lived during the
American Revolution which side would I
support? What would be my reasons?

_____

_____

_____

Why this is an interesting question or problem:

**Possible Answer** It gives me an opportunity
to investigate the American Revolution
in a truly personal way. I could view the
Revolution from my own vantage point and
make my own decisions, instead of simply
taking the side that the text might present.

Some other things I wonder about this question or problem:

**Possible Answer** Which side would
my classmates or my family support?
Would their decisions impact my own?

_____

_____

## Formulating Questions and Problems (continued)

My investigation group's question or problem:

**Possible Answer** Which side would we support if we lived during the American Revolution? What are our reasons? What opinions do we share? Where do we have differing opinions?

What our investigation will contribute to the rest of the class:

**Possible Answer** We will contribute to a class-wide decision on which side to support in the American Revolution. We may also have reasons that will give other groups or individuals ideas to consider.

Some other things I wonder about this question or problem:

**Possible Answer** Is the decision of my group affected by the opinions of others? Are my decisions affected by the opinions of others? Are these outside opinions beneficial?

Name _____ Date _____

# Timed Writing: Expository Writing

**Think**

**Audience: Who** will read your expository writing?

**Possible Answer** another student

**Purpose: What** do you want to tell with your expository writing?

**Possible Answer** why I love to go fishing

**Prewriting** **Use the Timed Writing Strategies to complete the following assignment. Start by circling the key things you are asked to do in the instructions. Then, list three details you want to include in your expository writing.**

Write a paragraph about your favorite hobby. Be sure to include at least one sentence that describes when you first started doing this activity. Also include two sentences that tell why you enjoy it. You have twenty minutes to complete the assignment.

1. **Possible Answer** I first went fishing with my uncle last year.

2. **Possible Answer** I like being outdoors.

3. **Possible Answer** I like eating the fish I have caught.

## Revising
**Use this checklist to revise your expository writing.**

- ☐ Did you clearly describe your first time doing the activity?
- ☐ Did your sentences show the reader why it is your favorite hobby?
- ☐ Did you use transition words to organize your paragraph?

## Editing/Proofreading
**Use this checklist to correct mistakes.**

- ☐ Are there any spelling errors?
- ☐ Do all sentences contain correct punctuation?
- ☐ Did you correctly use prepositions and prepositional phrases?

## Publishing
**Use this checklist to prepare your expository writing for publication.**

- ☐ If you have time, rewrite your paragraph neatly on a fresh sheet of paper.
- ☐ Hand in your completed Timed Writing assignment.

Name _____ Date _____

# Spelling

**Focus**

- **Irregular plurals** do not follow the regular rules for forming plurals. They do not end in -s or -es. Sometimes the base word spelling changes to form the plural, and sometimes it does not change at all: *child, children; salmon, salmon; person, people*

- **Compound words** consist of two smaller words that have been combined to form one larger word. These two words keep the same spelling in the compound word.

- Understanding and identifying suffixes and their meanings can help you determine the meaning and spelling of a difficult or unfamiliar word. Many words feature the suffix *-less*. *Less* is a word on its own, but is also a suffix that means "without."

**Word List**

1. children
2. moonlight
3. noiseless
4. shoemaker
5. salmon
6. wastebasket
7. sleeveless
8. halfway
9. people
10. earsplitting
11. sightless
12. quarterfinal
13. countless
14. tombstone
15. stainless
16. letterhead
17. tireless
18. flyswatter
19. friendless
20. showerhead

**Practice** The following spelling words are missing one of their base words. Write the missing part of the compound word in the space provided.

1. _____fly_____ swatter

2. tomb___stone___

3. _____quarter_____ final

4. _____half_____ way

5. ear___splitting___

6. letter___head___

7. _____waste_____basket

8. shower_____head_____

9. _____shoe_____maker

10. _____moon_____light

**On the line, write the spelling word that is formed by adding the suffix -less to each of the following base words.**

11. friend    friendless

12. stain    stainless

13. sleeve    sleeveless

14. noise    noiseless

15. tire    tireless

16. count    countless

17. sight    sightless

**Apply**    **On the line, write the spelling word that matches each definition.**

18. without sound    noiseless

19. without marks or dirt    stainless

20. without buddies or pals    friendless

21. with a lot of energy    tireless

22. too many to count    countless

23. without the ability to see    sightless

24. without sleeves    sleeveless

Name _____  Date _____

# Prepositions and Prepositional Phrases

**Focus**

A **preposition** shows the relationship between a noun or a pronoun and another word in a sentence.

A **prepositional phrase** is a group of words that begins with a preposition and ends with the object of the preposition.

**Example**

• We walked through the blinding snowstorm.

**Practice**  **Circle the prepositional phrases in this paragraph.**

Individual Chinese kingdoms began building what would become the Great Wall around the seventh century B.C. The wall was started in the northern part of the kingdom's capital. Other states started building walls for protection during the sixth century. In the third century B.C., the first emperor of China connected the walls into one system. The Great Wall extends 4,160 miles across China's countryside. Many tourists today still visit what remains of the wall.

**Apply**    **Write sentences using these prepositions in a prepositional phrase.**   Possible Answers

1. after _We went for ice cream after practice._

2. at _Hank roped a cow at the ranch._

3. from _Our puppy came from an animal shelter._

4. on _On our car's antenna, we have a flag of my dad's old school._

5. under _José skateboarded under a clear blue sky._

6. with _Tamika danced with her father at the wedding._

**Improve the paragraph below by adding at least four prepositional phrases to provide more information to the reader.**   Answers will vary.

         after school.
Jonah likes to skateboard ʌ He often goes with his brother.
            near the picnic tables
They prefer the lot next to the big oak trees ʌ Many kids come
    on the weekend         among the skaters
here to skate ʌ There is a lot of competition ʌ However, they
                       during the week
also enjoy teaching each other new tricks they learned ʌ Their
    beneath the shade of the trees
parents sometimes sit ʌ and watch them skate.

Name _____   Date _____

# Base Word Families, Suffixes *-ment, -able, -ful*

**Focus**

A **base word** can take many different forms when different prefixes, suffixes, and roots are added. When you know the meaning of the base word, you can begin to find the meanings of the words in the base word family.

- The suffix **-ment** means "an action or process, or the result of an action or process." The suffix usually forms nouns as in *government*.

- The suffix **-able** means "capable, having, or worthy of." *Reliable* means "one capable of being relied upon."

- The suffix **-ful** means "full of." *Beautiful* means "full of beauty."

**Practice**

The following words are followed by their base words. Write three more words with the same base word. Use the suffix listed in one of the derivatives. Use a dictionary if you need help.

**1. discovered** (-able)
Base word: cover
**Possible Answers** uncovered, recover, uncoverable

**2. agreed** (-ment)
Base word: agree
**Possible Answers** disagree, agreement, agreeable

**3. entrusted** (-ful)
Base word: trust
**Possible Answers** trusted, trusting, distrustful

**4. meaning** (-ful)
Base word: mean
**Possible Answers** meaningful, meaningless, meant

**Apply** Now write two sentences for each base word family from the previous exercise. Use the base word in the first sentence and one of the derived words in the second sentence. Possible Answers

**5.** cover: Be sure to cover your mouth whenever you cough.

word in the same family: I went to the lost and found to recover my hat.

**6.** agree: My friends and I agree that the school's French fries are too salty.

word in the same family: I made an agreement with my mother to clean my room on Saturday.

**7.** trust: You should always be able to trust your best friend.

word in the same family: Do not loan money to a distrustful person.

**8.** defense: There is no defense for rude or unkind words.

word in the same family: The criticism made him defensive.

Name _____     Date _____

# Selection Vocabulary

**Focus**

**looting** (lōōt' • ing) *v.* stealing valuable things from others (page 350)

**commander** (kə • man' • dər) *n.* a leader (page 350)

**invaders** (in • vād' • ərz) *n.* plural of **invader:** a person who breaks into something or some place without being asked or wanted (page 350)

**prompt** (prompt) *adj.* quick or on time (page 351)

**civilians** (sə • vil' • yənz) *n.* plural of **civilian:** a person not in the armed forces (page 353)

**revealing** (ri • vēl' • ing) *v.* making known (page 354)

**idle** (īd' • l) *adj.* not busy (page 354)

**lessen** (les' • ən) *v.* to make or become less (page 356)

**precautions** (pri • kô' • shənz) *n.* plural of **precaution:** something done beforehand to prevent harm or danger (page 356)

**portrait** (por' • trit) *n.* a likeness of a person that is created by a painter or photographer (page 360)

**Practice**  Tell whether the boldfaced definition that is given for the underlined word in each sentence below makes sense. Circle *Yes* or *No.*

1. Our <u>commander</u> let us finish the training early.
   **leader** ................................................................. Yes   No

2. Lily was <u>idle</u> while the rest of us worked hard.
   **quick or on time** ............................................. Yes   No

3. I hope the doctor can <u>lessen</u> the pain in my back.
   **to make or become less** ................................ Yes   No

4. The men were <u>looting</u> the art museum.
   **stealing valuable things from others** ........... Yes   No

**5.** Lorna is taking <u>precautions</u> against getting a sunburn.
**something done beforehand to prevent harm or danger** ............. Yes  No

**6.** We had <u>prompt</u> service at the new restaurant.
**not busy** ..................................................................... Yes  (No)

**7.** The <u>invaders</u> destroyed every house on the block.
**people not in the armed forces** ....................................... Yes  (No)

**8.** I painted a <u>portrait</u> of my grandfather.
**a likeness of a person created by a painter or photographer** ...... (Yes)  No

**9.** Fruits and vegetables are <u>revealing</u> to a healthy diet.
**important or necessary** ................................................. Yes  (No)

**10.** <u>Civilians</u> protect the citizens of a nation.
**Leaders** ..................................................................... Yes  (No)

**Apply**  Circle the correct word that completes each sentence.

**11.** John gave a _____ answer to the teacher.
(**a.**) prompt   **b.** invaders   **c.** mates

**12.** The ice should _____ the swelling in your ankle.
(**a.**) lessen   **b.** idle   **c.** prompt

**13.** The thieves are _____ and breaking windows.
**a.** idle   (**b.**) looting   **c.** revealing

**14.** The army asked the _____ to leave the area by midnight.
(**a.**) civilians   **b.** genius   **c.** portrait

**15.** Jordan is _____ the ending to the movie!
**a.** looting   **b.** mutually   (**c.**) revealing

**Name** _____    **Date** _____

# Drawing Conclusions

**Practice**    Skim the selection "The Master Spy of Yorktown." Then, next to each person's name below, write a statement (draw a conclusion) about him. Then, record the text clues on which you based your conclusions. **Answers will vary.**

The Marquis de Lafayette: _____

Clues: _____

_____

_____

_____

James Armistead: _____

Clues: _____

_____

_____

_____

**Apply** Write about a character, topic, thing, or event. Before you begin writing, identify a specific conclusion about your subject that you want readers to draw. Write a paragraph about your subject below. Then, exchange papers with a partner. When you have finished reading each other's papers, write a conclusion you have drawn and the text clues that support it at the bottom of the page.

Answers will vary.

_____

_____

_____

_____

_____

_____

_____

_____

_____

_____

_____

_____

Conclusion and Text Clues: Answers will vary.

_____

_____

_____

_____

Comprehension Skill • *Skills Practice 1*

Name _____ Date _____

# Making Conjectures

Our question or problem:
**Possible Answer** Can a nation be
formed peacefully?

_____

_____

_____

_____

Conjecture (my first theory or explanation):
**Possible Answer** I think other nations
formed through peaceful negotiations
and without violence.

_____

_____

_____

_____

_____

_____

As you collect information, your conjecture will change. Return to this
page to record your new theories or explanations about your question
or problem.

# Establishing Investigation Needs

My group's question or problem:

**Possible Answer** Can a nation be formed peacefully?

**Knowledge Needs**—Information I need to find or figure out in order to investigate the question or problem:

A. **Possible Answer** What other nations were formed peacefully?

B. **Possible Answer** How did that nation go about doing it?

C. **Possible Answer** When did they become independent?

D. _____

E. _____

| Source | Useful? | How? |
|--------|---------|------|
| Encyclopedias | yes | to find nations that were formed peacefully |
| Books | yes | for historical information |
| Magazines | | |
| Newspapers | | |
| Videotapes, filmstrips, and Audio clips | | |
| Television | | |
| Interviews, observations | yes | for a different perspective |
| Museums | yes | for historical information |
| Other: | yes | more historical information |

Table heading: **Possible Answers**

Name _____ Date _____

# Timed Writing: Summarizing

**Think**

**Audience: Who** will read your summary?   **Possible Answer**

someone interested in learning about James Armistead

**Purpose: What** is your reason for writing a summary? **Possible Answer**

I want to share with my readers a few details from James Armistead's life.

**Prewriting**   Use the Timed Writing Strategies to complete the following assignment. Start by circling the key things you are asked to do in the instructions. Then record three details from the selection that you want to include in your summary.

Reread page 291 of "The Master Spy of Yorktown." Write

a short paragraph summarizing the main idea contained

on that page. Be sure to include at least three of the most

important facts or events. You have twenty minutes to

complete this exercise.   **Possible Answers**

1. The Marquis's friendship with James made him join the fight against slavery.

2. The Marquis helped found an anti-slavery group in Paris.

3. The Marquis supported equal rights for the rest of his life.

## Revising  Use this checklist to revise your expository writing.

☐ Did you include a topic sentence at the beginning of your paragraph?

☐ Did you include only the most important details?

☐ Did you use your own words? Are any of your sentences too similar to those in the original selection?

## Editing/Proofreading  Use this checklist to correct mistakes.

☐ Did you check the spellings of proper names or specialized words against the original selection?

☐ Do all sentences contain correct punctuation?

☐ Are all prefixes, suffixes, and verb endings used correctly?

☐ Have you correctly used prepositions and prepositional phrases?

## Publishing  Use this checklist to prepare your expository writing for publication.

☐ If you have time, rewrite your paragraph neatly on a fresh sheet of paper.

☐ Hand in your completed Timed Writing assignment.

Name _____  Date _____

# Spelling

**Focus**

• Understanding and identifying suffixes and their meanings can help you determine the meaning and spelling of a difficult or unfamiliar word. The suffix **-able** means "inclined to," or "capable or worthy of."

• The suffix **-ful** means "full of." The suffixes -ful and -able both make the words to which they are added adjectives.

• The suffix **-ment** means "result or process," or "state or quality of," and is added to verbs to form nouns. When a suffix begins with a consonant, the base word usually does not change when the suffix is added, unless it ends with a *y*.

**Word List**

1. dependable
2. movement
3. beautiful
4. peaceful
5. experiment
6. reliable
7. reasonable
8. government
9. helpful
10. fearful
11. embankment
12. entertainment
13. agreeable
14. memorable
15. development
16. thoughtful
17. fruitful
18. fashionable
19. encampment
20. marketable

**Practice** **Add the suffixes -able, -ful, or -ment to the following base words or word parts and write the resulting spelling words on the lines.**

1. embank _embankment_

2. reason _reasonable_

3. thought _thoughtful_

4. fear _fearful_

5. help _helpful_

6. fashion _fashionable_

7. beauty _beautiful_

8. experi _experiment_

9. encamp _encampment_

10. market _marketable_

11. fruit _fruitful_

12. entertain _entertainment_

13. agree _agreeable_

14. govern _government_

15. peace _peaceful_

16. develop _development_

17. depend _dependable_

18. move _movement_

19. memory _memorable_

20. rely _reliable_

**Apply** Match each word to its definition.

21. dependable _H_    **A.** full of beauty

22. movement _D_    **B.** state or quality of being amused

23. beautiful _A_    **C.** able to be sold

24. peaceful _I_    **D.** state or quality of being in motion

25. experiment _J_    **E.** full of fruit

26. reasonable _N_    **F.** full of consideration

27. fearful _G_    **G.** full of fright

28. embankment _L_    **H.** able to have confidence in

29. entertainment _B_    **I.** full of calm

30. thoughtful _F_    **J.** process of testing

31. fruitful _E_    **K.** result of making camp

32. fashionable _M_    **L.** result of building a raised structure

33. encampment _K_    **M.** inclined toward clothing trends

34. marketable _C_    **N.** inclined towards clear thinking

**Name** _____ **Date** _____

# Electronic Technology: Creating Text

**Focus**

Today, most people write using word-processing programs. Creating a text is faster and easier to do once you have learned how to use **electronic technology.** Many schools and libraries have computers with word-processing programs available to the students.

**Practice**

Write about a classmate's favorite movie or book. First, choose someone to interview. Then listen carefully as he or she describes the plot of the movie or book. Be sure to ask questions to discover why your classmate liked the movie or book. Use the following lines to take notes. Answers will vary.

_____

_____

_____

_____

_____

_____

_____

_____

_____

_____

_____

_____

**Apply** Now use a word-processing program to write a paragraph about the movie or book. Be sure to tell why it is your classmate's favorite work. When you have finished, print your paragraph and read it to the class. Use the following lines to write an outline for the electronic text you will create. Answers will vary.

_____

_____

_____

_____

_____

_____

_____

_____

_____

_____

_____

_____

_____

_____

_____

_____

_____

_____

Name _____ Date _____

# Plurals and the Prefix *con-*

**Focus**

Most **plurals** are formed by adding -s or -es.

- For words that end in a consonant and *y*, change the *y* to *i* and add -es.
- For words that end in a vowel and *y*, just add -s.
- For some words that end in *f* or *fe*, change the *f* or *fe* to *v* and add -es.
- For words that end in a consonant and *o*, you add -es.
- For words that end in *o* preceded by a vowel, just add -s.
- For words that end in *s, z, ch, sh,* or *x*, just add -es.

- cherry, cherries colony, colonies
- key, keys
- wife, wives calf, calves
- potato, potatoes
- piano, pianos
- scratch, scratches

Many words feature the prefix **con-.** This prefix is from the Latin meaning "with, join, or together."

Connect = to join **with**, or establish communication with

Conspire = to join **with** another person or group sharing a common goal

**Practice**

Complete the following list by filling in the blanks with the correct singular or plural form of each word. Circle the words that contain the prefix *con-.*

| | Singular | Plural | | Singular | Plural |
|---|---|---|---|---|---|
| **1.** | month | months | **6.** | idea | ideas |
| **2.** | (confederation) | confederations | **7.** | wish | wishes |
| **3.** | consequence | (consequences) | **8.** | boss | bosses |
| **4.** | fox | foxes | **9.** | conjunction | (conjunctions) |
| **5.** | citizen | citizens | **10.** | hero | heroes |

**Write the word with the prefix *con-* on the line corresponding to its definition.**

| concede | consequence | contend |
|---------|-------------|---------|
| constrain | context | confederation |

**11.** Joined with a group of states

___confederation___

**12.** To force with restrictions in a strained or

difficult manner ___constrain___

**13.** The joining of text together so that it can

show its meaning ___context___

**14.** To cede, or yield, with hesitance

___concede___

**15.** To struggle with ___contend___

**16.** A conclusion made with logic, or following a

sequence of events ___consequence___

Name _____ Date _____

# Selection Vocabulary

**Focus**

**character** (kâr' • ək • tər) *n.* all the qualities that make a person or thing different from others (page 366)

**allegiance** (ə • lē' • jəns) *n.* faithful support of a country, person, group, or cause (page 367)

**central** (sen' • trəl) *adj.* main; chief (page 367)

**concern** (kən • sûrn') *n.* something important to a person (page 367)

**league** (lēg) *n.* a number of people, groups, or countries united for a common purpose (page 368)

**contribute** (kən • trib' • yo͞ot) *v.* to give (page 368)

**delegates** (de' • li • gəts) *n.* plural of **delegate**: a person who is chosen to act for others (page 368)

**eavesdroppers** (ēvz' • drop' • rz) *n.* plural of **eavesdropper**: a person who listens to other people talk without letting them know he or she is listening (page 371)

**accomplishment** (ə • kom' • plish • ment) *n.* achievement (page 372)

**rumors** (ro͞o' • mərz) *n.* plural of **rumor**: a story or statement passed from one person to another as truth with no proof (page 372)

**Practice** Write the vocabulary word next to the group of words that have a similar meaning.

**1.** stories; gossip _____ rumors _____

**2.** loyalty; support _____ allegiance _____

**3.** busybodies; listeners _____ eavesdroppers _____

**4.** main; most important; major _____ central _____

**5.** donate; give; volunteer _____ contribute _____

**6.** group; confederation _____ league _____

7. achievement; success __accomplishment__

8. important; worry __concern__

9. representative; person chosen __delegates__

10. quality; personality __character__

**Apply** Match each word on the left to its definition on the right.

11. league

12. eavesdroppers

13. central

14. delegates

15. accomplishment

16. concern

17. character

18. contribute

a. main; chief

b. a number of people, groups, or countries united for a common purpose

c. something important to a person

d. to give

e. people who are chosen to act for others

f. people who listen to other people talk without letting them know they are listening

g. all the qualities that make a person or thing different from others

h. achievement

Name _____ Date _____

# Research Report

**Audience: Who** will read your research report?

**Possible Answer** my classmates

**Purpose: What** is your reason for writing a research report?

**Possible Answer** I want to tell people about the Bill of Rights.

Note cards will help you organize the answers you find. On each card, record the details you will need later for your bibliography. Fill in the sample index card below to practice.

> *Bill of Rights*
>
> *First Amendment— Freedom of speech,*
> *freedom of press, freedom of religion,*
> *freedom of peaceable assembly, freedom to*
> *petition the government*
> *Second Amendment— right to bear arms*
> *Third Amendment— prevents government*
> *from quartering soldiers*
> *Fourth Amendment— unreasonable search*
> *and seizure*

**Possible Answers**

**Question:** What is the first amendment?

**Answers:** freedom of speech, press, religion, peaceable assembly,

**Type of source:** book

**Author:** Krull, Kathleen

**Title:** *A Kids' Guide to America's Bill of Rights*

**Pub. City:** New York

**Pub. Name:** Avon Books

**Pub. Date:** 1999

**Pages:** 12

## Revising   Use this checklist to revise your note cards.

- ☐ Did you rewrite the information you found in your own words?
- ☐ Did you include bibliographic information for each source?
- ☐ Did you use clear subject headings?

## Editing/Proofreading   Use this checklist to correct mistakes.

- ☐ Did you use quotation marks if you needed to quote an author's exact words?
- ☐ Did you check the spellings of proper names or specialized words against the original selection?
- ☐ Did you check proper nouns and quotations to make sure they are capitalized correctly?

## Publishing   Use this checklist to see if you are ready to begin writing your report.

- ☐ Do your note cards contain enough facts, examples, and explanations for you to be able to write an informative research report?
- ☐ Are your note cards organized so that your report will have a beginning, middle, and end?

Name _____     Date _____

# Spelling

**Focus**

• A prefix changes the meaning of the base word it precedes. Identifying prefixes and understanding their meanings can help you figure out the meaning and spelling of a difficult or unfamiliar word. The prefix **con-** means "with," or "together."

• The inflectional ending **-ing** is used in the participial form of verbs. These words can function as verbs, adjectives, or nouns. If a word ends in e, drop the e before adding the inflectional ending -ing. If a word ends in a y or x, the spelling of the base word stays the same when you add the inflectional ending -ing.

**Word List**

1. conform
2. conclusions
3. substituting
4. relaxing
5. concurrent
6. engineering
7. condense
8. liquidating
9. reducing
10. constrain
11. confirm
12. discharging
13. memorizing
14. delegating
15. configure
16. devastating
17. concave
18. marrying
19. concede
20. confront

**Practice**

On the line, write the spelling word that results when the prefix *con-* is added to the following base words or word parts.

1. cede      concede
2. cave      concave
3. form      conform
4. current   concurrent
5. clusions  conclusions
6. strain    constrain
7. firm      confirm
8. front     confront
9. dense     condense
10. figure   configure

**On the lines, write the spelling words that drop the final *e* before adding the inflectional ending -*ing*.**

11. substituting
12. liquidating
13. reducing
14. discharging
15. memorizing
16. delegating
17. devastating

**On the lines, write the spelling words whose base words do not change when adding the inflectional ending -*ing*.**

18. relaxing
19. engineering
20. marrying

**Apply** On the line, write the spelling word that is related by a common base or root word to each of the following words.

21. inform    conform
22. relaxation    relaxing
23. reduction    reducing
24. liquid    liquidating
25. strained    constrain
26. front    confront
27. married    marrying
28. conclude    conclusions
29. confirmation    confirm
30. memory    memorizing

31. conceding    concede
32. cave    concave
33. discharge    discharging
34. substitute    substituting
35. current    concurrent
36. engineer    engineering
37. devastate    devastating
38. condensation    condense
39. delegate    delegating
40. figure    configure

Name _____  Date _____

# Capitalization

**Focus**

- Quotations are capitalized when they are complete sentences or when they begin sentences.

- Always capitalize proper nouns, even when they are used as adjectives.

- Personal titles are capitalized only when they are part of a name.

- *A, an, the, but, and, to,* and *of* are not capitalized in titles unless they are the first or last word.

- Patrick Henry is remembered for saying, "Give me liberty, or give me death."

- Swiss watch
  Franklin stove

- my grandpa, our president
  Grandpa Miller,
  President Ford

- *In the Heat of the Night*
  Articles of Confederation
  *Everything on a Waffle*

**Practice**  **Circle the words that should begin with a capital letter.**

1. the fourth of july celebrates the signing of the declaration of independence.

2. our first president, general george washington, said: "it is better to offer no excuse than a bad one."

3. one of the few movies made about the american revolution is drums along the mohawk.

4. the book come to the cowpens! describes a battle between american and british forces.

5. a painting of founding father benjamin franklin hangs in the national portrait gallery in washington, d.c.

Draw three lines under each letter that should have been capitalized. Draw a slash through each letter that should not have been capitalized.

My brother, Brian, attends Thomas Jefferson high school. He is on the Soccer Team. Each labor day, a fundraiser is held to raise money for the Jefferson patriots' sports teams. Tables filled with donated items line the High School's hallways. Everything is for sale. The high school's Principal, Henry Showalter, kicked off the event by announcing, "let the sale begin!"

While the sale was happening inside, games and other activities were being held on the High School's front lawn. My brother's Coach sat in the dunking booth for a while. Brian took his chance, and his second toss sent coach Harris splashing into the water. It was the funniest thing I have ever seen!

**Name** _____ **Date** _____

# Comparatives and Superlatives

**Focus**

- A **comparative adjective** or **adverb** compares one person, thing, or action to another.

- A **superlative adjective** or **adverb** compares one person, thing, or action to several others.

- When forming the **comparative,** use the word *more* for most longer modifiers, or *most,* for the superlative instead of the *-er* or *-est* endings.

- I am **taller** now than I was two years ago.

- That is the **prettiest** painting in the museum.

- Tom was **more patient** than Jim. Of all her team members, Kyra runs **most quickly.**

**Practice** Write the comparative and superlative forms of each adjective and adverb listed below.

1. late    later, latest
2. low    lower, lowest
3. bright    brighter, brightest
4. fearful    more fearful, most fearful
5. bad    worse, worst
6. good    better, best
7. pretty    prettier, prettiest
8. famous    more famous, most famous

**Apply** Cross out the incorrect form of each comparative and superlative adjective and adverb in the following paragraph and write the correct form above it.

Animals are the ~~interestingest~~ *most interesting* and sometimes the ~~most strangest~~ *strangest* things on Earth.

Did you know that the Goliath beetle, weighing 3.5 ounces, is the ~~heavier~~ *heaviest* insect in the world? The sailfish, at sixty-eight miles per hour, swims ~~quickliest~~ *most quickly* of all fish. The Australian sea wasp has the ~~more painful~~ *most painful* sting of all animals. The two-toed sloth moves ~~slowest~~ *slower* than any other mammal and spends most of its life in trees. Howler monkeys yell ~~louder~~ *loudest* of all primates. Their voices can be heard up to three miles away.

Word Structure • *Skills Practice 1*

**Name** _____ **Date** _____

# Selection Vocabulary

**Focus**

**utter** (ut' • ər) *v.* To express out loud (page 326)

**declaration** (dek' • lə • rā' • shən) *n.* A written statement that makes something known (page 326)

**draft** (draft) *n.* A rough copy of something written (page 327)

**rights** (rīts) *n.* Plural of **right**: a just, moral, or lawful claim (page 328)

**bombarded** (bom • bärd' • əd) *v.* Past tense of **bombard**: to attack with bombs or heavy fire from big guns (page 329)

**retreat** (ri • trēt') *v.* To move back (page 329)

**debate** (di • bāt') *n.* A discussion between groups that do not agree (page 329)

**exposing** (ik • spōz' • ing) *v.* Leaving open or without protection (page 329)

**composition** (kom' • pə • zish' • ən) *n.* Something put together or created, especially something written (page 331)

**treason** (trē' • zən) *n.* The betraying of one's country by helping the enemy (page 333)

**Practice** Write *T* in the blank if the sentence describing the vocabulary word is true. Write *F* if the sentence is false. For every *F* answer, write the word that fits the definition.

**1.** A *composition* is a discussion between two groups that

do not agree. _____F_____ _____debate_____

**2.** *Treason* is betraying one's country by helping the enemy.

_____T_____

**3.** To *expose* is to express something out loud.

_____F_____ _____utter_____

**4.** When something is attacked with bombs and heavy fire from big guns, it is being *bombarded*.

_____T_____  _____

**5.** To *retreat* is to move back.  _____T_____  _____

**6.** A *declaration* is a rough copy of something written.

_____F_____  _____draft_____

**7.** *Compositions* are a just, moral, or lawful claim.

_____F_____  _____rights_____

**8.** A *declaration* is a written statement that makes something known.

_____T_____  _____

**9.** Leaving something without protection is *exposing* it.

_____T_____  _____

**Apply**  **Review the vocabulary words and definitions from "Give Me Liberty!". Write three sentences using the vocabulary words provided. Possible Answers**

**10.** debate  I had a debate with my friend about which basketball team was better.

**11.** composition  Jamilla had to write a composition about the book she had just read for her English class.

**12.** treason  Benedict Arnold committed the most famous act of treason in American history.

**Name** _____   **Date** _____

# Main Idea and Details

Authors organize their writing into a **main idea** supported by **details.**

- A main idea should be clear and focused.
- A main idea should have supporting details. Details provide additional information about the main idea.

**Read the paragraph on page 331 that begins "Congress then turned . . ." and answer the following questions.**

**Possible Answers**

1. What is the main idea of this paragraph?

   Jefferson's original wording of the Declaration of Independence

   was changed by Congressional delegates.

2. Write three details from the paragraph that support the main idea.

   a. Whole paragraphs were taken out, and new words and phrases

   were added.

   b. In all, nearly one hundred changes were made.

   _____

   c. John Adams thought that some of the changes were good but

   that some of Jefferson's best writing was taken out.

**Apply** Write a paragraph for each of the two topic sentences provided below. Use sentences for each paragraph that support the main idea stated in the topic sentence.

**Topic 1.** Sentence: Thomas Jefferson's writing of the Declaration of Independence was influenced by what he had already read about individual rights.

**Possible Answer** Jefferson had read the writings of philosopher John Locke. Locke argued that people were born with certain natural rights. Jefferson had also read Thomas Paine's Common Sense, a popular pamphlet in colonial America. He would have known that Virginia and some other states already had declarations of rights.

**Topic 2.** Sentence: At first the colonies were not united in their desire to declare independence from Britain.

**Possible Answer** The first vote had only nine colonies voting for independence. Pennsylvania and South Carolina changed their votes the next day. A short time later, Delaware joined the others. New York never opposed independence, but its delegates took two weeks to decide. Finally, the vote was unanimous.

Name _____ Date _____

# Research Report

**Audience: Who** will read your research report?

**Possible Answer** my classmates

**Purpose: What** is your reason for writing a research report?

**Possible Answer** I want to tell people about the Bill of Rights.

**Prewriting** Use this example of a bibliography to cite multimedia sources used during your investigations.

---

**Bibliography**

BOOKS: Author (last name first). Title of Book (underlined).

City of Publication: Publisher, Copyright date.

INTERNET: "Post Title" (in quotations). Site Title (underlined).

Post date or last update. Site sponsor. Date accessed.

<electronic address>

---

**Multimedia sources can help with your research. They can also make your report more informative and more interesting to your audience.**

**Now think of two ways to use multimedia sources to enhance your research report. For each idea, list a place where you could look for that source.**

**1.** What: **Possible Answer** a copy of the original Bill of Rights

Where: **Possible Answer** on the Internet

**2.** What: **Possible Answer** a painting of James Madison

Where: **Possible Answer** in a book at the library

## Revising    Use this checklist to revise your multimedia sources.

☐ Do you have materials from multimedia sources in one of the following formats: graphics, audio, or video?

☐ Will the multimedia sources help enhance your paper?

☐ Have you prepared the materials from multimedia sources that you will use?

☐ Are there any additional multimedia sources you could include?

## Editing/Proofreading    Use this checklist to correct mistakes.

☐ Do you have the information you need to list your multimedia sources in a bibliography?

☐ Have you clearly labeled each photograph, map, or other illustration so that your audience knows what graphic they are seeing?

## Publishing    Use this checklist to prepare your multimedia sources for a research report.

☐ Decide if your multimedia sources will be used in a paper, during a presentation, or both.

☐ Meet with your teacher to discuss which multimedia sources will work best for your classroom.

Name _____  Date _____

# Spelling

**Focus**

- A **comparative adjective** or **adverb** compares one person, thing, or action to another. A **superlative adjective** or **adverb** compares one person, thing, or action to several others. Example: *I am **shorter** than my sister. I am the **shortest** in my family.*

Form the comparative by adding *-er* to the base word, or the word *more* to most longer modifiers. Form the superlative by adding *-est* to the base word, or the word *most* to most longer modifiers. Follow the "drop-the-e rule" and "change-the-y-to-i rule" when adding these endings.

- **Synonyms** are words with the same, or nearly the same, meaning. A word may have many synonyms that have slightly different meanings.

**Word List**

1. opposed
2. against
3. prettier
4. prettiest
5. jubilant
6. exultant
7. younger
8. youngest
9. disaster
10. misfortune
11. greater
12. greatest
13. nourishment
14. sustenance
15. funnier
16. funniest
17. decrease
18. diminish
19. livelier
20. liveliest

**Practice**

Add *-er* or *-est* to the following base words to form the comparative and superlative spelling words.

1. lively + *-er* = livelier
2. lively + *-est* = liveliest
3. young + *-er* = younger
4. young + *-est* = youngest
5. pretty + *-er* = prettier
6. pretty + *-est* = prettiest
7. great + *-er* = greater
8. great + *-est* = greatest
9. funny + *-er* = funnier
10. funny + *-est* = funniest

*Skills Practice 1* • Spelling

On the lines, write the spelling words that are synonyms for the following words or phrases.

**not in favor of**

11. opposed

12. against

**thrilled**

13. jubilant

14. exultant

**hardship**

15. disaster

16. misfortune

**lessen**

17. decrease

18. diminish

**food**

19. nourishment

20. sustenance

 **Apply**

On the line, write the spelling word that correctly completes the sentence. Use the base word in parentheses plus a comparative or superlative ending.

21. That show is (funny) than the previous one. funnier

22. My father is the (young) of all his brothers. youngest

23. Is the dress over there (pretty) than this one? prettier

24. Is Fluffy (young) than Spot? younger

25. *Dancing Shoes* is a (lively) song than *Sad Sadie*. livelier

26. Was that the (great) movie you have ever seen? greatest

27. Who is the (funny) person you know? funniest

28. That is the (pretty) baby I have ever seen. prettiest

29. Is one trillion (great) than one quadrillion? greater

30. Chirpy is the (lively) of all our birds. liveliest

Name _____   Date _____

# Electronic Technology: Revising Text

**Focus**

Today, most people write using word-processing programs. **Revising a text** is faster and easier to do once you have learned how to use electronic technology. Many schools and libraries have computers with word-processing programs available to the students.

**Practice**

1   2   3   4   5   6   7   8   9

**1.** You want to remove a paragraph. After you have highlighted it, you click
_____6, Cut_____.

**2.** To place the paragraph in another part of the text, you click
_____7, Paste_____.

**3.** You decide you do not want the paragraph there after all.
You click _____8, Undo_____.

**4.** To save your work, you click _____3, Save_____.

**5.** To open a file you saved earlier, you first need to click
_2, Open existing file_.

**6.** You have finished revising and editing, but you want to check the
spelling of your work. You click _____5, Spell-Checker_____.

**Apply** Type these two sentences on a computer: "Thomas Jefferson did not want to write the Declaration of Independence. He wanted John Adams to write the first draft." Using the toolbars on the computer, scramble the two sentences together. Finally, pass your scrambled sentences to a partner and have him or her unscramble the sentences using the toolbar.

Answers will vary.